A Most Haunting Castle

A Most Haunting Castle

Writings From the Ruins
at Berry Pomeroy

Edited by Bob Mann

For Brian

Best wishes

Bob

Longmarsh Press

Published by Longmarsh Press 2012

Longmarsh Press, 5 Brook View, Follaton, Totnes, Devon TQ9 5FH

www.longmarshpress.co.uk

A CIP catalogue record for this book is available from the British Library

ISBN 978-0-9561705-2-1

Printed and bound by Veasey's, Totnes

Cover picture of Berry Pomeroy Castle by Barbara Kuyuate

Cover design by Michelle Melhuish

Layout petercowlam@petercowlam.me.uk

This book is dedicated, not without a little trepidation, to the White and Blue Ladies

Totnes Aug 2012

Acknowledgements

MANY THANKS TO Laurence Green, who first suggested a book of writings inspired by the castle; Peter Cowlam, for editorial and technical support; Catherine Smith, and all the other authors, who responded so enthusiastically to my request for work.

Thanks also to Fran Cello; Barbara Kuyuate; Michelle Melhuish; Kathy and Rob at the Bay Horse, who patiently endured nightly discussions of Berry Pomeroy Castle, sometimes joining in, and to Rob for the final version of the title; Sam Richards; William Graves and Patrick Villa for quickly providing all I needed to know about Robert Graves and the castle; Maya Hussell for similarly telling me about the Elizabeth Goudge connection; members of Berry Pomeroy Parish Church, who put on an exhibition of Jack Hazzard's pictures at exactly the right time; Pruw Boswell-Harper for details about pre-Reformation 'churching'; Jill Drysdale and Sue King at Totnes Museum Study Centre; and anyone who has talked to me about their experience or knowledge of the castle.

And thanks, of course, to Ellen Mann (1923–2002), for taking me there in the first place.

Finally, I must express deep gratitude to the various tutelary deities and protective forces who hover above and around the castle, and who have fortuitously put me in the way of books, information, contacts and other kinds of help, just as I needed them, often with a sense of timing I can only describe as mystic.

Bob Mann, from my study, Totnes, 2011

Contents

The Authors

Helen Ashley moved to Devon in 1982, and the countryside of Dartmoor was a strong influence on her early poetry. Her work combines a life-long love of words with the way in which memory and the imagination work together with our everyday experience to enhance perception. She is involved in several poetry groups in the South Hams and Torbay. Her poems have appeared in a variety of magazines and her first book, *Ways of Saying*, was published by Acumen Publications in June 2010. She currently lives in Totnes with her husband, Mike Hannaford.

Valerie Belsey is best known for leading guided walks and for her books on highway history and green lanes. The latest of these, *Exploring Green Lanes and the Stories they Tell: South and East Devon*, puts the emphasis on the stories, real and imagined, which were told by travellers along these ancient routeways. It was the winner of the Devon History Society's Recommended Book of the Year Award. When training to be a teacher she made a study of the folk songs of Devon and has recently set up the Beesounds Acoustic Music Festival where tunes and songs which tell stories can be heard by the sea.

Her story shows how fame, fortune and happiness can sometimes arise from unexpected directions.

Anna Eliza Bray (1790–1883), novelist and pioneer folklorist, is usually known as 'Mrs Bray of Tavistock.' She was the author of the first Dartmoor novel, *Fitz of Fitz-ford* (1828), and *Henry de Pomeroy* (1841), amongst others.

Peter Cowlam is the author of literary fiction, plays and poetry, and has travelled extensively. His last major research trek took him halfway round the world to Auckland, New Zealand. Here he took the opportunity to track down the first writer and scholar to be granted unlimited access to the Nabokov archives, Vladimir Nabokov's biographer Brian Boyd. A mildly epiphanic moment arrived at a reading in the Dead Poets Bookshop on the

Karangahape Road, where one of Brian's ex-students, a fixer and bibliophile, was able, he said, to arrange a meeting. What was sought was a seat at a café table, where Brian would drink his latte and indicate whether, in his opinion, *The Original of Laura*, the novel Nabokov was working on at his death, would ever be published. Nabokov died in 1977, having issued strict instructions that the manuscript be destroyed. For reasons too complex to elaborate on here, that latte was never drunk, and Peter returned to his life in the UK, where for its two and a half issues he edited *The Finger*, a journal of politics, literature and culture. He has two novels in print, and more recently a novella, *Marisa*. His latest play, *Who's Afraid of the Booker Prize?* is published by New Theatre Publications. He is, incidentally, very happy to learn that after its thirty years in a Swiss bank vault, *The Original of Laura* was published by Penguin in 2009. See www.petercowlam.info.

Laurence Green was educated at King Edward VI Grammar School and King Edward VI College, Totnes, and has a master's degree from Exeter University. He writes ghost stories and biographies, including *Great War to Great Escape*, a recently published book on his grandfather's role in The Great Escape from Stalag Luft III in 1944. He is presently working on a biography of Charles Causley, the Cornish poet. He is often to be found sleeping on a bench in his garden at Ashprington, when not writing ghost stories or articles for Cornish magazines.

Deborah Harvey lives in Bristol with four interesting offspring and a Border Collie called Ted. Her first poetry collection, *Communion*, was recently published by Indigo Dreams, and will be followed by her novel, *Dart*, in 2012.

Sue Hinds was born in Newbury but has lived most of her life in Devon. She works as a Registrar after a career as a Bank Manager. She is currently writing poetry for the angling press and a novel inspired by the castle. She endeavours to go beyond the anecdotal and descriptive to evoke feelings and sensory perceptions; the castle's setting has given her a perfect base for that structure.

Idris W. Izzard is a new writer and the tale in this collection is his first published story. For anyone overcoming the ruts of the past, the future is a wide-open book, and it is his profound wish to write many another adventure on its endless pages.

Anna Lunk is a Creative Writing and Literature tutor based in Totnes. Her stories have appeared in *Grey Sparrow Journal* and *Riptide*. She is currently trying to place a novel about a film camerawoman, *Flight*, and is working on a novel about an early 20th century garden designer set on the Welsh border. Anna enjoys writing site-specific pieces for radio and open mic evenings.

Bob Mann has written guides, histories, stories and countless articles and reviews for newspapers and magazines, including all two and a half issues of *The Finger*, of which he was also co-editor. He founded and edited *The Totnes Historian* for Totnes Museum Society (until the notorious 2004/5 edition), and was editor of *Wyrd*, a magazine of strange phenomena, which lasted for four whole issues. He has also been Folklore and Dialect Recorder for the Devonshire Association. He established the Longmarsh Press in 2008 to publish his own work and that of other Devon writers, and is well known as a leader of guided walks, including the Totnes Ghost Walk. Much of his work derives from a deep sense of connection with South Devon, its landscapes, history, folklore and traditional culture, as well as his feeling of responsibility for the area's future.

Debbie Miller-Wright was born in Surrey in January 1975. She moved to Devon in 2004, and to Totnes in 2005. She is Pub Witch at the Bay Horse Inn and a self-employed Kickboxing Instructor and Personal Trainer.

Edward Montague was the author of *The Castle of Berry Pomeroy* and, according to the title page, also of *Montoni, or the Monk of St Benedict* etc.

John Prince (1643–1723), born near Axminster, was vicar of Totnes from 1675 to 1681, when the Seymours invited him to Berry Pomeroy, which then included Bridgetown. He stayed until his death, writing and publishing *The Worthies of Devon* (1701), a colourful celebration of his native county and the numerous great men it had produced until that time. It has long been valued by local historians and genealogists. More recently, Prince has become well known locally for the sexual scandal that nearly lost him his living, but his book, as far as we can know, is more interesting than his love life.

Wendy Ruocco grew up in Paignton, where she still lives. Her father instilled into her a deep love and respect for the town and surrounding countryside. She runs the Quo Vadis restaurant with her Neapolitan husband, Michele, as well as writing and painting. In 2007 she published a romantic novel, *Dark Knights of Compton Berry*, the first of a trilogy, which is set mainly at Berry Pomeroy Castle. See www.quovadis-ruocco.co.uk.

Pamela Sandry Gorman lives in Dartington within view of Yarner Beacon, with which she feels a deep soul connection and which features in many of her paintings. She also works in ceramics, collage, printmaking and jewellery. Her poems and photographs appear in *Dartington Catch* (2010), co-written with Simon Williams and Susan Taylor, arising from a poetry walk around Dartington Hall gardens during the Ways With Words literary festival. One of her poems in this book, 'The White Lady,' has been displayed at the castle café, alongside a photograph she took of a tree in the nearby woods; the form of a young woman is clearly visible in the trunk.

Catherine Smith describes herself thus: hair of a tiger; heart of a dragon; voice of a fishwife; soft as a kitten.

We all have memorable firsts (our first romantic kiss, our first funeral, etc.). **Ken Taylor** recalls a personal first at Berry Pomeroy Castle – his first encounter with a roosting bat. It was an amicable meeting although perhaps rather one-sided as the bat displayed no clear emotion, while the young writer was clearly thrilled. That was in the 1970s and although the castle's bats may have developed a more interactive policy toward visitors since then, Ken suspects they will still not share many of the castle's nocturnal secrets with a mere passing acquaintance... Despite having had non-fiction books translated into four European languages (and, of local interest, *Dartmouth Ghosts & Mysteries*, published by Richard Webb in 2006), this is Ken's first published account of his meeting with what to him will always be *The Bat of Berry Pomeroy Castle*. See www.wavewrights.com

Susan Taylor is a widely published poet with a keen interest in local culture and history. Devon projects include: *Crossing Time*, poetry collection celebrating the pixy stories of William Crossing on his centenary; *Reclaiming the Myths of Dartmoor*, with Simon Williams, Julia Thomas and Howard Frey – award winning folklore, folk song and music show and CD; *Voices Off* – commissioned poems and song for Ways With Words about the South Devon fishing industry; *Kitty Jay Speaks* – for Exeter University's 'Hidden Histories' project; *Earthed,* with Mike Edwards and Simon Williams – haiku sequence on geology and pottery on Dartmoor; *Taking Time*, with Carol Ballenger and Graham Hodgson of Arts Live – Dartington Primary's children's poetry workshops, producing two haiku photo books. Her poems can be found on Fresco Poetry Chairs at Agatha Christie's house, Greenway, at Galmpton and at Dartington Hall, during the summer months. For more, see www.susantaylor.co.uk.

Simon Williams trained as an engineer, but in 1981, with his wife and fellow poet Susan Taylor, he took up the post of Arvon Foundation Centre Co-Director at Totleigh Barton, in North Devon. Since 1985 he has been a professional journalist and lives in a hamlet on the southern edge of Dartmoor. He has had four published poetry collections, the latest of which is *Quirks*, from Oversteps Books, in 2006. He has just published a collection of Clerihews, a poetic form he is hoping to re-popularise.

A Place of High Strangeness
Bob Mann

THE STORY, I feel, ought to commence in a solemn, old-fashioned, even rather portentous manner. Maybe, with apologies to John Cowper Powys and other favourite writers, something like this:

On a certain mellow afternoon in September, a little over forty years ago, a woman and two children might have been observed alighting from a green Western National omnibus onto the narrow road which winds between thick Devon hedges from Berry Pomeroy to Marldon, at the point where a lane leads off to the left, and a signpost directs the curious traveller to the ancient ruins of Berry Pomeroy Castle. Something must have occurred at that moment: a sympathetic vibration, too tenuous and elusive to be fully apprehended; a strange connection, made or remembered, between the mysterious forces that pervade the environs of the castle and the consciousness of one of the children, which has – through chains of causality impossible, with our present knowledge of the universe, to unravel – resulted in the book which you now hold in your hand.

I remember it all clearly. It was 1968, and I was about two months short of my 10th birthday. My sister, Fran, was two years younger. I remember the brief walk up the hill, and the group of old stone cottages, at one of which our mother paid for us to go in, and how we entered through the gateway onto the gradually descending wooded drive, and into the dream.

I remember the dappled sunlight as we walked along, and the first, sudden view of the castle rising before us, grey and massive. Although the thick ivy that covers the ruins in 19th and early 20th century pictures was no longer there, this was still before the excavations and restorative work of the 1980s, and the courtyard, as we went in through the towering gatehouse, was grass-grown and uneven, full of mounds and tussocks, with some strange little wooden seats dotted around. We went into the gatehouse, where there was, at that time, no hint of a hidden 15th century wall painting, and descended to the rooms on either side (which cannot be called 'dungeons,' because they are not underground), and then into the narrow passage leading off to one side for as far as we could. It was there that I had a sense of past movement, and seemed to hear ancient voices somewhere ahead of me, at the end of the passage. We went along the Ramparts Walk, also grass-grown at that time, to St Margaret's Tower, and the little room at the bottom (which isn't a dungeon either, of course), and then into the main mansion. I remember the fireplace in particular, and how we peered up out of the gloom into the clear sky.

We thoroughly explored the castle, and walked three times, backwards, around the Wishing Tree. I remember gazing vertiginously down into the valley below the cliff on which the castle stands; a Land Rover moving along the road from the mill seemed like an intrusion into, or out of, a different age.

We went to the old-fashioned wooden tea room, where we acquired a guide book and a little yellow pamphlet called *Ghost Stories and Legends of Berry Pomeroy Castle* by S. M. Ellis. We were at the castle for a good two or three hours, going everywhere in and around the ruins at least once, and some parts of them more than once, before finally walking back along the drive towards home.

Presumably there was no convenient bus, because we just went down through the village and onto the main road back to Totnes, but we were used to walking. I can even remember the taste of some old-fashioned sweets that we had with us (my father drove a lorry around the area, delivering them to shops), but mainly I remember how my mind, as we came along the pavement from True Street to the top of Bridgetown, was full of images and impressions of the castle, many of which are still with me. When I think of the place it is always as it was on that day, all grey and green and neglected, rather than as it is now.

That is my honest recollection of my first encounter with Berry Pomeroy Castle. I found it strange and fascinating, unlike anywhere I had ever experienced. I may have felt a certain anxiety about the ghosts, and a desire to protect my mother and sister from any baleful influence, but I think this probably grew over time, as I brooded on the place, and pondered the stories in S. M. Ellis's little book.

My mother was a sub-editor and feature writer for the *Totnes Times*, and like any good journalist she decided to use the visit to earn a shilling or two. She wrote an article about the castle and our excursion to it, which appeared a week or so later. I vaguely remember the article, but have not seen it since that time. If she kept a copy, I have yet to find it amongst the things of hers

2

that I have, and unfortunately the files of the paper from late 1968 to 1971 are missing from the otherwise complete collection in the Study Centre at Totnes Museum, probably because the *Totnes Times* in that period was owned by an eccentric gentleman who renamed it the *Devon Times Guardian*, which no one ever called it.

So I have little to go on, but I think she made much of the fact that Fran and I were quieter than she expected us to be, and that we picked up on the strange atmosphere which pervades the castle. She may have exaggerated for effect, but I don't remember any feelings at the time of being misrepresented, which, I confess, I did sometimes have about other things she had written; she also published children's stories in women's magazines, and occasionally put us into them. I do recall that the following week there was a letter from a local farmer, who described Mrs Mann's experience with 'her two boys' (sic) as 'tommy-rot' (or maybe it was 'poppy-cock'), because he had walked past the castle on many a dark night, and never seen or felt anything, which obviously meant that no one else could either.

§

About ten years later, browsing in the second hand bookshop that used to be next to Totnes Museum, I picked up for 20p *A Gazetteer of British Ghosts* by Peter Underwood (1971). This is still a standard work, and has been much quarried into for countless other books and articles. Underwood must have sought out recent material on the places he was writing about, or maybe a local correspondent sent him a copy of my mother's piece, because it was with interest and growing irritation that I read, in his section on Berry Pomeroy, of how in 1968 a woman had taken her two children, aged nine and seven, to the castle 'for a picnic', expecting them to 'romp and explore and enjoy themselves.' Instead they had stayed 'sedately' by her side, and when they did finally venture into the ruins, they soon ran back to say that it was 'horrid,' and that they wanted to go home.

I'm sorry, but that is just not how it was, and that word 'horrid' has always particularly annoyed me – it was far too genteel for us. I wrote at the time in the margin of Underwood's book that, as far as I remembered, it was only later that the fear developed.

Without actually being able to compare Peter Underwood's version with my mother's article, I have to concede the slight possibility that he wasn't writing about us at all, and that another woman, in the same year, took two children of the same ages to the castle, and either told him directly about their experience, or left an account of their visit in the public domain, which he subsequently used; but I had no doubt, when I first read it, that he was describing us, though very inaccurately.

But every story takes on a life of its own, and this one soon began to be repeated or referred to in other sources. It was a contemporary tale to go with the more traditional ones, and over the years I have become used to seeing versions of it. Sometimes it was copied more or less verbatim from Underwood, though even then it was often exaggerated: by the time Judy Chard got hold of it for *Devon Mysteries* (1979), we were refusing to leave our mother's side, and 'begging' to be taken home. Other writers have turned the story into a general law: *Haunts and Hauntings*, published by the AA in 1974, stated baldly that 'visitors, especially families with young children,' often remarked on the 'desolation' of the place, and that 'nobody' stayed at the castle very long. Nobody?

Keith B. Poole, in *Britain's Haunted Heritage* (1988), which has an atmospheric picture of the castle on the cover, reports that the area of St Margaret's Tower has 'strangely affected' children playing nearby, who have run away to other parts of the 'profusely scattered ivy-clad ruins.' Ivy-clad, in 1988?

In February 2011, whilst beginning to work on this introduction, I emailed Fran to ask what she remembered of that first visit, and she wrote back:

> All I remember is feeling quite quiet, as if I didn't want to wake anything up. Strong memory of the trees as well. I felt I also wanted to revisit, as I felt that there was more to discover. Remember the air being really fresh and a little cold away from the sun.

All right. So we were quiet. Absorbed by the mysterious atmosphere of the place. Maybe slightly subdued. But we were there for the whole afternoon, and the human mind changes constantly; I certainly don't think we could have been very cowed as we sat outside the café, drinking bottles of Pepsi-cola and burping gassily, much to the horror of our mother and a nearby elderly lady. We just didn't want to run around playing and 'romping,' that's all.

This is not, of course, to say that Berry Pomeroy Castle is any less strange or frightening than everyone says it is, simply a warning against recycling second or third hand information. Because the place really has haunted me since that day, exerting a fascination and a pull, and sometimes a repulsion, which I have never experienced in relation to anywhere else.

S. M. Ellis's little paper-covered collection of stories probably has a lot to answer for. I have a copy before me now, with its eerie illustration on the front. It is a mere eight pages long. There is no publication date, but it was on sale for many years, maybe decades, and untold numbers of people must have bought and read it (though it can still be found in second hand bookshops, the frailty of its format means that, as time goes on, it will become rarer, so pick one up when you get the chance). The nature of folklore is that it exists in multiple versions, none of which can ever be thought of as 'definitive,' but her tellings of the tales are as close to being so as anyone's can, at least for my generation (I know it's 'her' because on the back, in small print, it says 'compiled by Mrs S. M. Ellis;' I also suspect, from their use of certain words and phrases, that her booklet may have influenced some of my contributors to this volume).

The ghostly ladies; the brothers who spurred their horses over the cliff rather than submit to their enemies; the two working men from Totnes who dreamt of a crock of gold buried in the huge fireplace: they all sunk into my imagination and, now I think about it, were probably the first stories I ever read in which I could visualise precisely the very locations in which they were supposed to have happened.

Best known is the tale of the two sisters, Eleanor and Margaret, in love with the same man. Eleanor, mistress of the castle, locked her more beautiful sister up in a dungeon, and starved her to death, and now, on moonlit nights, the lovely shade of Lady Margaret, the White Lady, rises from St Margaret's Tower and glides along the Ramparts Walk, beckoning to anyone who sees her to join her in the depths below. Unfortunately, those who do see her are likely to die soon afterwards.

I was appalled by this story, and troubled by its implications, which worried me far more than the actual visit to the castle had done. For years I dreaded being told that anyone I cared about was going there, or even thinking of going there, because I didn't want them to see the ghost and die. This still seems to me a perfectly reasonable concern. But though I developed a fear of the place, I was still strangely drawn to it, if not physically then in many other ways. I somehow always knew it was there, just a couple of miles away, over the fields, even without consciously thinking about it.

There were little things, but they got bigger. One of the windows in St Margaret's Tower has two bars in it, and I never liked to see a window thus divided, either in reality or in a picture: the sight of one took me straight back there. I tried to avoid the names Margaret and Eleanor, and even the words 'beckon' or 'beckoning,' because they immediately made me see the ghost on the ramparts. Fortunately, neither Margaret nor Eleanor was an especially fashionable name at the time: I can remember only one Margaret in my year. I don't know how I'd have managed if the Pomeroy sisters had been called Jane and Susan, or Mandy and Karen, or Jackie and Dawn... but they weren't, and the story wouldn't work if you tried to substitute any of these names.

I became aware that a large area of woodland on the hillside above the River Dart, as seen from our home in Bridgetown, could be interpreted as a reverse image of the castle: I could clearly make out the two towers of the gatehouse, and the square shape of the mansion stretching away from it, but from right to left instead of left to right. Forty-three years of growth and decay have altered the formation, but I can still point the simulacrum out to you, and maybe enable you to see it as well: the gatehouse is fairly obvious, although the mansion behind is less even than it was.

From the age of thirteen I played with Totnes brass band, and once, after we had performed well at a contest, the landlord of the Bay Horse Inn invited us all for a celebratory drink. To get around the fact that many of us were under-age, the party was held in an upstairs room at the back of the pub, which was used as one of the two local lodges of the Royal Antediluvian Order of Buffaloes – the Berry Castle Lodge, to be exact; the banners and artefacts, the great buffalo horns and photographs of men in weird regalia, and just the name of the lodge, all made it, in my mind, like a strange extension of the castle itself, a tentacle of unease reaching into the safe heart of the home town.

I came to associate the castle with a piece that we played, an arrangement by Eric Ball of Leon Boellmann's romantic *Suite Gothique* for organ. Each of its four movements seemed to perfectly express something about the place, and even now, whenever I hear it, or find it running in my head, it is accompanied by images of Berry Pomeroy. I can easily imagine a film of the castle, with that music as the soundtrack.

My mother had taken us walking around Totnes from our earliest years, and in my teens, at weekends and holidays, I rambled happily alone, wandering far in every direction, through the lanes, fields and footpaths. I was frequently aware of the hidden presence of the castle, over there somewhere in the woods. Through reading, I had come to appreciate something of its status as a Romantic, 'Gothic' ruin, and in spite of myself was drawn ever closer; I circled it, and sometimes came nearly within sight. I remember a Sunday afternoon in December, almost seeing it from the woods, and hearing strange cries that could have been animal or human; I hastened home for tea, and whichever Victorian novel was being dramatised at the time (Andrew Green, in *Our Haunted Kingdom*, published in 1973, says that a crying baby is often heard at the castle, though no one else mentions this).

But it was not until one day in 1976 that I finally found myself seeing the castle again from the lawn: it was a damp, warm, muggy day, and there it was, in front of me, in all its mystery. I didn't have the money to actually go in, so I never again explored the ruins before all the restoration and archaeological work that began soon afterwards, and which revealed, amongst much else, the wall painting in the gatehouse, a late 15th century Flemish-style Adoration of the Magi, and the bases of the Jacobean colonnade in the courtyard, previously hidden by all those mounds and tussocks. I remember I did walk out there early in 1977 with the intention of looking around, but it was already closed for the work to begin, so I contented myself with buying an old print from the café (the 1829 one by E. Finden after W. Westall, showing the castle from the Gatcombe valley, for those who like to know these things).

I have been back countless times since then, alone and with other people. I have led walks to and around the castle, and written about it in articles, stories and guides. In the 1990s I wrote several books on South Devon places for Obelisk Publications of Exeter, and it forced itself into all of them, even the ones about Buckfastleigh and Ivybridge, where it had no obvious reason to be (the publisher, Chips Barber, who had his own strange tales to tell – he had, in fact, seen the White Lady – made no comment). I have recorded a cassette of its stories, legends and ghostly experiences, and even appeared there once on breakfast television. Naturally, I dream of the place frequently, and though it may change its appearance and location, its essential nature is always recognisably the same. I have gradually acquired all the guide books and novels written about the castle, and there are images of it around my home in the form of antiquarian prints, photographs and postcards of all ages. It is depicted on a mug in which I keep loose change in the kitchen, and I also have it on bookmarks, fridge magnets and a key ring. Outside, by the fence, is a piece of the Wishing Tree, which I was given after it was partially felled in 2009 for safety reasons; the log features in two short tales which I sent to friends in lieu of Christmas cards, one of which appears later in this book. I can clearly visualise the castle before me now, as I write. I'm not obsessed with the place, or anything, you understand.

But many people do get obsessed with it, going there as frequently as possible, often until something happens that drives them away, never to return. Others are compelled to create artworks about it or delve into its mysteries. Most of you reading this book will have picked it up casually when you saw it, because you thought it might be interesting, or maybe you know me, or one or more of the people who have contributed poems and stories. But there will be some amongst you who, the minute you learnt of its existence, had no choice but to get hold of a copy as soon as possible, just as you would anything else concerning the castle and its lore. You know who you are. And you can be pretty sure that the White Lady does, as well.

§

So, what is this extraordinary place?

Berry Pomeroy Castle occupies a dramatic cliff-top site, hidden by dense woods, about two and a half miles from Totnes in South Devon. There are very few points in the surrounding area from which even a small part of it is visible, unless you are actually in front of it, or in the Gatcombe valley below, which feels right, and adds to the castle's sense of mystery and separation from ordinary life. From the heights around Totnes you can look across at the gentle, rounded landscape of green and flesh-pink hills and fields, and see where it is: the red-tiled roof of the barn, by the entrance to the drive, stands out clearly in this area of grey roofs, but there is nothing to show that the deep woods stretching away beside it contain anything unusual. The castle is within a medieval deer park, the solid stone walls of which still run dramatically across the fields. It is quite separate from the actual village of Berry Pomeroy.

The manor of Beri was given after the Norman Conquest to Ralf de la Pomerai, who came from the village of la Pommeraye near Falaise. Almost everyone who has written about the castle, at least until very recently, has assumed that Ralf fortified the site, and that the present ruins are in direct descent from a Norman or at least early medieval structure, but it has now become clear that this is not the case. Though the Pomeroys were owners of the estate for nineteen generations, and may have sometimes lived at the manor house in the village from the 13th century, they had many other land holdings in Devon and Cornwall, and there is no evidence of any building on the castle's site before the late 15th century, the first documentary reference dating only from 1496. It is not really much of a castle at all, in the purely defensive sense, more a fortified manor house; able, perhaps, to protect its occupants from modest attacks, but not from a full-scale military offensive. Anyone familiar with the great castles of Wales or other parts of England will find it decidedly underwhelming, in this respect.

I say that the castle's age has now become clear, but some people actually knew it a long time ago: in 1897 the Totnes solicitor and historian Edward Windeatt read a paper at the castle to the Teign Naturalists' Field Club, in which he described a visit in 1882 by members of the British Archaeological Association. After thoroughly inspecting the ruins, these learned gentlemen agreed unanimously that there was no trace of anything earlier than the late 15th century. It took another hundred years for this to be rediscovered and widely accepted. People obviously wanted the castle to have a longer and more interesting history, and projected their assumptions and fantasies onto it: even Pevsner, in his original South Devon volume, and Hoskins, in his great history of the county, got the dating wrong.

In 1547 the castle was bought from the Pomeroys by Sir Edward Seymour. He was the older brother of Jane Seymour, third wife of Henry VIII. Later he became the Duke of Somerset and, as Lord Protector, ran the country during the short reign of his nephew, the boy-king Edward VI. His son and grandson, both called Edward, spent large sums of money creating a palatial mansion within the Pomeroy walls (though they did not inherit the Dukedom: that title went, for several generations, to another branch of the family). This ambitious project was never completed, and the castle was finally abandoned at the end of the 17th century, the family moving to their estates in Wiltshire, which were more convenient for London. By 1701 the vicar of Berry Pomeroy, John Prince, could write of the castle: ''tis now demolished.' Although folklore accounts for its ruinous condition as being caused by Parliamentarian bombardment during the Civil War, or a great fire, or both, there is no physical or written evidence for either. It is still owned by the Seymour family, in the person of the present Duke, but in 1977 it was put into the safekeeping of the Department of the Environment, now English Heritage.

So Berry Pomeroy Castle was not actually a living, working building for all that long: not much more than two centuries. It has been a ruin now for longer than it was a home, and many more people have experienced it as an ivy-covered, Romantic pile, or, more recently, as a 'Heritage' site, than ever saw it as an inhabited castle or mansion.

Tourism, as we know it today, began in the late 18th and early 19th centuries, when the British nobility and gentry, denied access to the continent by the Napoleonic Wars, began to discover the wilder regions of their own islands. They were soon joined by the rising professional and middle classes. Their sensibilities were strongly influenced by the taste for 'Gothic' novels set in Catholic southern Europe, featuring ancient castles hidden in thick forests and filled with dungeons, tunnels and secret rooms. These tales involved imprisoned heiresses, faithful lovers, evil monks and nuns, and the castles swarmed with ghosts and apparitions, portents and omens.

This is the context for the growth of the legends, as much as any truly local folklore. When early visitors to the fashionable new resorts of Torquay, Teignmouth and Exmouth were driven into the Devon countryside in search of the Picturesque and Romantic, Berry Pomeroy Castle was about as close as they could get to the settings they were familiar with from the novels of Ann Radcliffe, Mathew Lewis, the Plymouth-born Eliza Parsons and the rest. Its only rival in Devon, as the archetypal 'Gothic' ruin, was Okehampton Castle (ironically, of course, Berry Pomeroy is not really gothic, in architectural terms, at all). Artists loved it: Turner, Girtin, Cox and Farington, along with thousands of amateur water colourists, all strove to reproduce its drama and mystery (see the excellent book by Smiles and Pidgely, *The Perfection of England: Artist Visitors to Devon c1750–1870*, for a fuller account). Images of the castle were disseminated widely by means of prints and engravings, and, later, by postcards (and, eventually, by fridge magnets).

Having said this, it must be admitted that the castle ruins are not particularly beautiful or even, really, very imposing, except from below. They fit almost awkwardly into their setting. The strange fascination that the place exerts, for so many, clearly lies in something other than any purely aesthetic appeal.

Ghosts, Saints and Scholars,
or 'Whose Tower is it Anyway?'

In the early summer of 2011, when I was already well into writing this introduction, English Heritage published a new guide to the castle by Charles Kightly. Naturally, I went out there at the earliest opportunity to get hold of a copy. It is well-written, visually impressive, clearly organised, and is the first 'official' publication to comfortably incorporate the legends and ghostlore into the overall story, making it an excellently rounded, contemporary look at the castle in all its aspects.

As I write, it is still possible to buy the previous guide, by archaeologist Stewart Brown, first published in 1997. This, too, is a good, well-illustrated introduction to what is known of the history and architecture, all put clearly into context. Stewart Brown is also the main author of the most thorough study that is likely to be produced for a long time, in the 'Proceedings' of the Devon Archaeological Society number 54, 1996 (though not actually published until 1998). The whole volume, of over 350 pages, is devoted to the castle, and enshrines the results of all the excavations and researches from 1980 to the 1990s.

You should have all of these, as well as the two books by Deryck Seymour. He was a church organist and music teacher from Torquay, distantly related to the castle's owners, who produced, at his own expense, scholarly histories of Upton parish and Torre Abbey. In 1982 he published *Berry Pomeroy Castle*. In the very first sentence he admits to having been fascinated, indeed haunted, by the castle all his life. Stonemasons who worked on the restorations in the late 70s and early 80s remember a tall, white-bearded figure walking about, or sitting by the bushes next to the tea room, busily writing; I have a feeling he was there that day in 1977, when I bought the old print at the café. His book is marvellously illustrated by Jack Hazzard, who was the foreman of the works at the time (many of his drawings and paintings were left to Berry Pomeroy Church, where an exhibition of them was held in the Spring and Summer of 2011).

I could not rest until I had this book (I persuaded the editor of the *South Devon Scene*, to which I regularly contributed, to get me a review copy). It is a masterpiece, a detailed study of all that was known or could be surmised, at that transitional period, about the buildings, although some of its conclusions have now been proved wrong. It also covers the history of the Pomeroy and Seymour families in relation to the manor and castle, as well as the folklore and the hauntings, and some, though not all, of the literary works apparently inspired by them. It is out of print, but not difficult to find second hand. It is one of those books I shall always have near me, and if I disagree with the author later over various points, no disrespect is intended. He wrote what he knew.

Obelisk published his short book *The Ghosts of Torbay* in January 1990, and a couple of months later they brought out *The Ghosts of Berry Pomeroy Castle*, which has replaced the S. M. Ellis pamphlet as the indispensable text, and is still in print.

Berry Pomeroy Castle is, of course, best known for being haunted. This is the one thing that everybody who has heard of it is aware of, and the place is often described as the most haunted in England. For a long time, English Heritage were rather coy about this, discouraging their staff from talking about the ghosts to visitors, but they finally recognised the futility of such an attitude, and decided to utilise, rather than fight, the castle's reputation, especially when they realised that it could be turned to their economic advantage. They even held ghost tours in the summer of 2006, and allowed paranormal groups in for vigils.

If somebody tells me they have seen a ghost, or experienced anything out of the ordinary, I do them the courtesy of believing them, even if I don't necessarily agree with their interpretation of what they saw. But even the most sceptical is likely to feel overwhelmed by the weight of evidence at Berry Pomeroy. As Deryck Seymour's ghost book shows, the range of strange phenomena experienced by all kinds of people at the castle is remarkable, and we probably all have a weird tale to tell of the place, or know someone who has. Hardly needing to stop and think about it, I can name friends, and other people I have talked to, who have seen glass in the windows, faces at windows or figures moving about the buildings and in the courtyard; they have heard ghostly sounds and smelled ghostly smells. Many have heard medieval or renaissance music, and even seen the musicians. They have suffered camera and engine failure. Some are simply unable to stay at the place, or even go near it. I recently heard of someone who insisted on being taken there, but then refused to get out of the car. This 'unreasonable fear,' as Seymour calls it, can suddenly affect people who, minutes before, were happily wandering around. Together with the strange attraction the castle has for many people, often operating at great distances, it is the commonest experience. For some of us, as you have gathered, the fear and attraction go together.

I remember my first real visit after all the changes began, in 1982, shortly after reading and reviewing Deryck Seymour's first book – hereafter referred to as 'Seymour (1)'. I wanted to show the castle to my partner at the time, Kate, as she had never been there. I was also interested to see what my reaction to the building work and excavations would be, and the fact that it was now in the hands of the government (a government which, I seem to recall, I was not especially keen on). I quickly realised that these things made absolutely no difference to the essence of the place, nor have any subsequent alterations, whether new walls, the roof on the gatehouse, wooden walkways, interpretation panels, the ticket office, audio-tours or anything else. However often I see them, in my mind the castle is always as it was in September 1968, and always will be. When I think of the Ramparts Walk, it has grass on it, while flowers and crack plants sprout profusely from the old walls. I suspect that those who knew the place early in the 20th century, when it was thickly coated in ivy, had the same experience after this was removed.

But I hated being there that day, not because of anything that had been done, but because I was weighed down by a feeling that something awful was about to happen to Kate, and that I had to protect her by getting her away as quickly as possible. She felt nothing of this, and, anyway, was well able to take care of herself.

The anxiety continued as we walked down through the field behind the tea room to the old mill, which at the time contained a gift shop selling pictures and souvenirs of the castle, S. M. Ellis's book of stories and, less predictably, lots of RAF and Battle of Britain memorabilia. The owner was clearly reliving his flying years: we wandered around to the accompaniment of marches and theme tunes from old war films, all growling, thundery basses and high flute trills like crying seagulls. Together with the threatening, oppressive atmosphere I was already feeling, this made it a very weird afternoon indeed.

But that mill, and the whole area of the Gatcombe valley below the castle, is weird anyway. Readers of both Seymour books will know of the experience of two ladies who went back in time there, and I have spoken to people who have described it as being pervaded by an invisible dark cloud. I felt it that day, and on several occasions since. There was an afternoon not long ago when, having come down the steep path from the castle lawn to the ponds, I just could not walk along the road to the mill. At other times, I can do it quite happily.

I have also directly witnessed the camera failure. Some time over the Easter weekend of 1990 I met my mother, my sister Fran, and Fran's then husband, Neil, for lunch in a Totnes pub. Afterwards, we decided quite spontaneously to go to Berry Pomeroy Castle, to see the newly restored painting in the guardroom, and any other changes that had been made. It was probably my idea: I had just been given Deryck Seymour's ghost book – hereafter referred to as 'Seymour (2)' – to review for the *Totnes Times*, and hoped to record some vivid experience of the castle's strange power. I had intended to go there quietly on my own and absorb the atmosphere, but the thought of us all being there together, again, appealed to my sense of continuity.

Perversely, I felt absolutely nothing; we could have been at any busy tourist place anywhere (well, almost). Fran, however, felt an unaccountable pressure to her temples, and, though she is an expert photographer, found that her camera refused to work, for no obvious reason. We walked around sedately by our mother's side, then sat outside the tea room (*not* drinking Pepsi), and I'd love to tell you that, while we were there, we overheard someone describing how, in 1968, a woman had taken her two children, aged nine and seven, to visit the castle, expecting them to romp and play...

The most famous ghosts at the castle are the Blue and White Ladies. What is interesting about them is that people still see them. This is unusual. The traditional ghosts of folklore, the headless horsemen driving carriages fashioned from bones, the evil monks, the gliding ladies in crinoline and the rest, seemingly embedded into the very fabric of Britain's old buildings and monuments, are rarely, if ever, actually encountered.

In real life, if someone sees a ghost, it is usually a vague, shadowy figure, and the whole experience is strangely inconsequential. There is no ready-made story to account for the apparition. The folkloric ghosts, on the other hand, have well-rounded tales attached to them, and are sometimes known historical figures. Berry Pomeroy is one of the few places where the traditional ghosts are apparently still active.

What exactly they are is beyond the scope of this book. I do not personally think that ghosts are the disembodied spirits of the dead. That is just the conventional assumption, and the problem is that it polarises: you either have to believe it, or dismiss the subject entirely. But there are many possible explanations for the sort of experiences people have at Berry Pomeroy and other haunted sites. Some apparitions may be recordings of past events onto the environment, replayed under the right atmospheric conditions: the imprint on wood and stone of powerful experiences and emotions, or what a Buddhist friend beautifully calls 'karmic footprints.' I am aware of the theory that hauntings and other paranormal happenings are often associated with places which have suddenly lost their importance, so that the psychic energy built up over years, maybe centuries, of continuous human activity, is left in a vacuum and gets out of control, which certainly fits the history of Berry Pomeroy Castle. I am sure, anyway, that when someone encounters a ghost, the experience is as much about that person, and their inner worlds, as it is about the place, or anything that may have happened there. We are intimately connected with our surroundings, after all, made literally of the same elements, but we each relate to an environment in our own unique way. For what it is worth, I have noticed that a lot of especially haunted sites are on limestone, as, indeed, is Berry Pomeroy Castle.

The Blue Lady is said to have been a Pomeroy daughter who bore a child to her own father, smothered it and now walks restlessly through the ruins. She also lures unsuspecting men to dangerous parts of the castle. She is usually identified as the ghost seen at the end of the 18th century by a young doctor, Walter Farquhar (1738–1819), who eventually became a baronet and physician-in-ordinary to the Prince of Wales, later George IV.

The story, which appears in a rare volume published in a limited edition in 1902, *Annals of the Seymours* by H. St Maur (some members of the family revived the ancient spelling in the 19th century), has been told many times, but is worth repeating because of the doctor's vivid description of the lady's expression. He was practising in the newly fashionable upper-class resort of Torquay, and one day was called to see the wife of the steward at Berry Pomeroy Castle, which still had a few habitable apartments. Whilst waiting, he saw a beautiful young woman pass through the room. She wrung her hands in distress, and, he recalled, 'if ever human face exhibited agony and remorse: if ever the eye, that index of the soul, portrayed anguish uncheered by hope and suffering without interval: if ever features betrayed that within the wearer's bosom there dwelt a hell, those features and that being were then present to me.' He naturally asked the steward who that sad looking girl was, but the man just became extremely agitated, convinced that his wife was going to die, which, of course, is what happened.

A great story, but just to show how problematic all this can be when you actually start looking into and comparing various accounts of the hauntings, S. M. Ellis describes the lady seen by the doctor as wearing white; but she only paraphrases his account, rather than quoting directly. Without easy access to *Annals of the Seymours* it is difficult to know what he did say about her clothing, if anything. Deryck Seymour (2) takes this apparition to be the Blue Lady, and he had read the book, so it seems safer to go with his version.

Charles Kightly, however, in the new guide, reckons that the story could not have happened at all. He reproduces the picture of the castle by Samuel and Nathaniel Buck, drawn in 1734, to argue that the whole place was uninhabitable long before the time of Dr Farquar's supposed visit. Their engraving certainly presents us with a devastatingly bare ruin, as does John Prince's elegiac description of 1701. So was the whole thing an elaborate joke, by the doctor himself, or the author of the 'Annals'? I find this difficult to accept, just because it seems such a pointless thing to do, and, as others have suggested, the Bucks may not have been aiming for topographical or architectural accuracy so much as wanting to create a particular impression of a ruined war-like stronghold, giving, for instance, crenellations to St Margaret's Tower which it may never have had. But whether the doctor's story is true or not, people still see the Blue Lady.

The White Lady is always identified as the Lady Margaret of the traditional story, the girl imprisoned in the tower by her jealous sister, a tale for which there is absolutely no historical evidence, but which is now as much a part of the castle as the very walls themselves. Even people who have never been to the place seem to know the story. I'm almost surprised that flowers and other presents aren't left for her in the tower, like at Jay's Grave on Dartmoor (possibly they are, and English Heritage staff quickly remove them every evening; if it hasn't happened yet, I'm sure it can only be a matter of time...).

The earliest mention I have found of her, purely as a visible apparition, is in *Bygone Days in Devonshire and Cornwall* by Mrs Henry Pennell Whitcombe (1874), who describes the tower, 'rising above some broken steps that lead into a dismal vault,' and then quotes from *Bentley's Miscellany* of 1867: 'The tale still runs that on certain evenings in the year, the spirit of the Lady Margaret, a young daughter of the house of Pomeroy, appears clad in white on these steps, and, beckoning to the passers-by, lures them to destruction by a fall into the dangerous ruin beneath them.'

Nothing here, you'll notice, about her being imprisoned: just an unromantic tumble down the steps for anyone who fancies her and gets too close.

According to Deryck Seymour (1), the Reverend Prince was the first to call it 'St Margaret's Tower' in print, in 1701. Seymour takes this to mean that, by then, 'the poor lady had become beatified.' It doesn't actually mean that at all (and I think he was being facetious – no one was beatified in 17th or 18th century England, and as a good historian he would have known this; beatification, anyway, is one step short of sainthood). What it means is that the story is obviously later than the name of the tower.

A few years ago English Heritage, in the guide book before Stewart Brown's, tried to rename it 'the Margaret Tower,' presumably because they were embarrassed by the idea of the girl in the story being described as a saint, a title they obviously didn't think she deserved. The Pevsner and Cherry volume on the buildings of Devon does the same, as did a friend of mine who used to work at the castle. Charles Kightly, in the new guide, uses both versions, just to be safe. But they are all missing the point.

The tower is not named after this fictitious young woman from a folktale at all. If it were, it would be called 'Lady Margaret's Tower.' It is called 'St Margaret's Tower' because it is named after St Margaret. It could only have been given that name before the Reformation, which means during the time when the Pomeroys were still here. The story of a girl imprisoned by a jealous sister belongs to an ivy-covered Gothic ruin, dark and mysterious in the moonlight, not to a newly finished building, at the heart of a busy estate, and home to a leading local family who are deeply involved in the administrative and economic life of the area. The name has to pre-date the story, and probably by centuries.

So maybe we should look for a minute or two at the person the tower is really named after.

St Margaret of Antioch was one of the most popular female saints in England during the late middle ages, appearing regularly on rood screens together with saints Catherine, Barbara and Agatha (none of them appears on the Berry Pomeroy screen, unfortunately, but there's a good one at Manaton, on the eastern edge of Dartmoor, which has Margaret and Barbara). They were beautiful, virtuous young women, living in the 2nd or 3rd centuries, who were martyred horribly for refusing to give up their faith or yield their virginity: Catherine, of course, was broken on a wheel, Agatha had her breasts cut off and Barbara was beheaded; we'll come to Margaret's fate in a minute. It is a relief to learn that they were all completely mythical, which is why the Catholic Church dropped them in 1969.

Margaret was especially revered, as she was responsible for protecting women in pregnancy and childbirth (if this seems a strange function for a virgin, just bear with me for a moment, if you'll excuse the expression). She was a shepherdess who spurned the advances of the Roman governor of Antioch in Syria, and was tortured, then *thrown into a dungeon*. Whilst imprisoned, she was visited, and finally swallowed, by the devil, in the form of a dragon. But even this failed to defeat her – through making the sign of the cross, she burst forth triumphantly from the dragon's belly, hence her connection with giving birth.

They then tried unsuccessfully to burn and drown her, before finally cutting off her head. About the only thing they didn't do was starve her.

Now, assuming any part of the story is that old, everyone in the 15th or early 16th centuries would have immediately associated a girl called Margaret, imprisoned in a dungeon, with the saint. It doesn't mean they thought she was the saint, or deserved to be one; it just means the connection was there. It would be enough. Deryck Seymour (1) states 'it seems that in folklore the name of Margaret is always attached to an imprisoned maiden.' If this is true, and I'm not aware of any other examples, the reason can only be the association with the saint. But I think we should forget about the girl imprisoned by her sister for a little longer, and stay with St Margaret.

She protected women in childbirth, so maybe one or more of the Pomeroy ladies had reason to be grateful to her, and thus dedicated the tower. Perhaps a room in the tower was used for the confinement of women. It literally was confinement, for a month or more after the birth. The mother was then 'churched,' a ceremony by which she was received back into the faith after the 'sin' of bearing a child; just as the baby, born with the 'original sin' of Adam, had to be baptised as soon as possible, so the woman had to be cleansed of the 'sin' of carrying an un-baptised baby. If, as seems now to be generally accepted, the room over the gatehouse was the castle chapel, then her first journey after giving birth would be along the Ramparts Walk towards it. This is, of course, the direction in which the ghostly lady is supposed to go. I have been told that it is reasonable to assume that the mother would have been wearing something white, possibly a veil; in a 16th century church inventory there is a record of a 'churching cloth fringed with white damask.' Could a folk-memory of this have contributed to the legend?

There is no evidence that the Pomeroys did use the tower for the confinement of women, so all this is pure speculation (it fits strangely, however, with something experienced by several women at the castle a few years ago, but the sensitive nature of the phenomenon prevents me from saying any more without their permission).

Stewart Brown, in the Devon Archaeological Society volume, treats the tower purely as a defensive structure, with gun emplacements in the lowest room and accommodation for the garrison upstairs, though I am pleased that he respects its ancient name, both in this and in his castle guide. It is true that the tower's original function was defence, as the castle was clearly built during the period of dynastic struggle and lawlessness later known as the Wars of the Roses. But after Henry Tudor took the throne, the age of powerful magnates with their own armies was definitely over, and a gun-tower in a private manor house, in remote Devonshire, would have been an illegal anachronism.

Deryck Seymour (1) states correctly that Prince, in his description of the castle, says that many gentlemen formerly held their lands from the tower, implying that the family used at least a part of it for business purposes. St Margaret, however, was concerned neither with defence nor the granting of charters, so the idea of it also containing a birth chamber is maybe worth considering. Rooms in buildings go through many changes of use over time, and in a ruin it is often impossible, without documentation, to know what a particular space has been used for. After all, the room above the gateway was turned into a chapel. If using what had been a guardroom, complete with portcullis, for this purpose seems incongruous to us, it is only because we forget that time in the past took as long as it does now. We tend to think of a particular century in a few instant images of people and events; to really appreciate it as a span of years takes an effort of the imagination. The sixty odd years – roughly three generations – between the accession of Henry VII and the purchase of the castle by Sir Edward Seymour gives plenty of time for a defensive structure that is no longer needed to become something else: a chapel in the case of the gatehouse, and an office, with perhaps a birth chamber, in the case of the tower. (But the old gun emplacements were still there, down below, just in case).

I offer the thought, anyway, as a contribution to the discussion. The tower was named after St Margaret for a reason, and it must have been a meaningful and practical one for those who used it.

After the Reformation, the saints and their stories disappeared quite swiftly from the English consciousness, only returning, in a far lower key, in the mid Victorian period, with the Anglican High Church movement and the restoration of the Roman Catholic heirarchy. Even the dedications of parish churches, so much a part of their identity today, were largely forgotten or disregarded during this time.

But occasionally something, maybe part of a story, or just an associated image, remained in the folk-memory. In Ashburton, for example, they have the legend of Cutty Dyer, an evil water-spirit who haunts the area around the King's Bridge over the River Ashburn, in the centre of the town. He seems to have originated with a large figure of St Christopher that once stood near the river crossing, to protect travellers during floods caused by the heavy moorland rains.

The process can also be seen in the changing status of holy wells. During the middle ages many of them were dedicated to female saints, and were places of serious pilgrimage. Later the well, often called something like Ladywell or Lidwell, became merely a place to leave offerings and make a wish, while the saint was transformed into a Grey or White Lady ghost haunting the vicinity.

In the late 18th and early 19th centuries, when Romantically-inclined travellers were discovering the castle, only a few antiquaries or members of old recusant families would have known anything about St Margaret, but I have no doubt that people were seeing the White Lady, or at least experiencing strange phenomena of various kinds at the castle.

If there's a ghost, there has to be a story behind it, and it won't be long before somebody remembers one, or makes one up. So maybe the locals recalled that there was something about a young woman being kept in a dungeon, and the tale, as we know it, began to develop. It is not so much Lady Margaret Pomeroy becoming a saint, as St Margaret of Antioch becoming Lady Margaret Pomeroy. But I am sure that there is more to the White Lady than either of them…

The main guide to the castle for many decades was *Berry Pomeroy Castle: an historical and descriptive sketch*, by A. E. and T. C. Mortimer. The various editions are never dated, but it was probably written in the late 1870s or early 80s, and continued to be reprinted until well into the 20th century. In it, the authors make an interesting error, if that is what it is. They refer to the 'traditionary supposition' that 'the gloomy basement chamber' of St Margaret's Tower was where 'the proud Lady Eleanor de Pomeroy, once mistress of the Castle, was confined for a lengthened period by her fair sister, through a feeling of jealousy.' (I love the word 'traditionary,' and the way in which the rather pompous style peters out so weakly with that 'through a feeling of jealousy.'). Why did they, alone of all who have written about the castle, put the wrong sister in the dungeon?

No one ever seems to have picked this up, but it is worth looking at. Is there a reason why the name Eleanor could be associated with young female incarceration, as we have seen that there is for Margaret?

Well, some believe, and it is a belief, rather than anything that could be proved, that the ghostly ladies who abound in folklore are symbolic representations, or psychic visions, or just convenient ways of describing, the ancient Celtic goddess Elen or Ellen (sometimes, later, conflated with St Helen or Helena). Many see her as an embodiment of the land and its energies. Without getting lost here in a discussion of leys, earth mysteries or psychic questing, about all of which I am more sceptical than some of my friends would like me to be, it is true that many people feel at Berry Pomeroy Castle and its surrounding terrain a sense of evil, of something not right. I have felt it myself, as you have read. The ghostly ladies, if they are manifestations of the earth goddess, seem to be the goddess gone bad. The energy of the land is clearly not flowing correctly; indeed, it has been imprisoned, and starved…

Whether you literally believe this, or just think of it purely as poetic imagery, you must admit it seems rather apt.

But, pleasing and intriguing as this playing around with names and ideas may be (and we need to remember that the thoughts above are all 20th and early 21st century conceptions, not 18th or 19th century ones), I fear that there is a more mundane reason for the Mortimer brothers placing Eleanor in the tower, which we shall come to in due course.

Probably Some Writer
Just Made It Up

Charles Kightly states confidently that many of the castle's legends derive from 19th century works of fiction, and that the White Lady 'originates' in a Gothic novel published in 1806, *The Castle of Berry Pomeroy*, by Edward Montague.

Now, I happen to be convinced that a great many 'traditional' (or 'traditionary') ghosts and legends are not, in fact, anything of the kind, but the innocent inventions of 19th and early 20th century poets or fiction writers, which have been taken as genuine folktales and retold in ever-changing variations. Students of folklore and the paranormal do not always have much knowledge of the more obscure byways of literature, but if they did, they would often find that the ghosts they are hunting actually first took form in the mind of some long-gone author.

Obviously I'm a writer, so I would say that, wouldn't I; we all like to emphasise the importance of what we do. But sometimes you can see it happening. The 19th century novelist William Harrison Ainsworth (1805–82) had an influence on the popular imagination of this country far greater than his current literary status suggests. In *Rookwood* (1834), he single-handedly invented the story of Dick Turpin's ride from London to York in one night, on a horse called Black Bess, celebrated ever since in numerous pubs along the route (many of which he is said to haunt), and firmly believed in by millions of people as a true historic occurrence. But Black Bess never existed, and Turpin, in reality, was a vicious thug from Essex who was part of a gang involved in armed robbery, rape and housebreaking, and who was eventually hanged for sheep and horse stealing. Thanks almost entirely to Ainsworth, he is one of Britain's most recognisable folk-heroes, the Gallant Highwayman, a status his recorded behaviour as a human being certainly does not merit.

Another of Ainsworth's novels was *Windsor Castle* (1843), which draws on the folklore of Herne the Hunter. It was illustrated by George Cruickshank, one of whose engravings shows Henry VIII encountering Herne's ghost in Windsor Great Park, an entirely imaginary scene, existing only in Ainsworth's mind. Most people who read the book when it came out probably understood that it was fiction, but by the time Antony D. Hippisley Coxe wrote *Haunted Britain* (1973), this knowledge could no longer be assumed. He refers to Herne's haunting of the Windsor area, and reproduces Cruickshank's picture, but without saying that it is an illustration from a novel; he merely states that it shows 'Herne the Hunter appearing to Henry VIII.' A few years later, in *Royal Hauntings* (1987), Joan Forman writes of 'the tradition' that Henry saw the ghost, and mentions Hippisley Coxe's use of the picture. She goes on to say that she has found no other reference to the tradition, but presumes that Cruickshank 'knew of it.' Well yes, because he'd been asked to illustrate the novel in which the meeting occurs. There was no 'tradition' at all.

By the way, the only full-length biography of Ainsworth, published in 1911, is by someone called S. M. Ellis, and that is nothing but pure coincidence.

M. R. James's story *A Warning to the Curious*, which concerns three ancient crowns buried on the Suffolk coast to protect England from invasion, and is entirely his invention, has been collected as a genuine piece of folklore and published as such (in Enid Porter's *The Folklore of East Anglia*, 1974), while, closer to home, it is often said that Arthur Conan Doyle was inspired by the legend of wicked Squire Cabell of Buckfastleigh when he created *The Hound of the Baskervilles*, but in fact the stories of Cabell and his tomb, in Buckfastleigh churchyard, only started being told after the novel was published in 1902.

To digress for a little longer: I have myself pointed out that one of the Westcountry's best-known ghostly incidents sprang solely from the imagination of one of my favourite writers, the Welsh mystic and weaver of weird tales, Arthur Machen (1863–1947). It involves that most famous of Devonian relics, Drake's Drum. Book after book, and article after article, has repeated the story of how, on the morning of the German fleet's surrender at the end of the First World War, the officers and crew of the *Royal Oak*, a ship manned largely by sailors from Devon and Cornwall, heard the incessant sound of a beating drum. Searches were made, but every man was accounted for; the bandroom was locked, and there was nowhere for a drummer to be hidden. Gradually it dawned on them that they were hearing the sound of the old sea-dog's famous drum, beating out to mark the triumph of Britain's navy over the enemy.

It is extraordinary that so many authors, including well-known folklorists and historians, have accepted this as a true event, or at least as an honest account of what was genuinely believed to be one. But for an entire ship's company to experience, together and at length, in a perfectly sealed environment, such a vivid and appropriate auditory hallucination, would have been unprecedented in the annals of psychical research. The captain and officers, and as many of the men as possible, would have been carefully interviewed and asked to sign witnessed statements, and the case would have been proclaimed as one of the greatest pieces of evidence for the scientific reality of the supernatural. This did not happen, because the whole thing is a story by Arthur Machen.

He is best remembered for his decadent horror novel *The Great God Pan* (1894), and his masterpiece of intoxicating prose, *The Hill of Dreams* (1907), but during his lifetime he was most famous as the author of a short story published in 1914 called *The Bowmen*. Even his admirers recognise that it is not much of a story, but it caught the mood of the times. It describes how British soldiers, fighting against heavy odds, are suddenly aided by ghostly fifteenth-century archers. This tale gave rise to the legend of the Angels of Mons, who demonstrated heaven's support for Britain and her allies by appearing in the sky above the battle. Machen insisted that he'd made the story up, but people insisted that it was true, and that they knew someone who had been there. Countless articles, and several books, have explored the legend and all its ramifications and meanings.

Machen followed *The Bowmen* with similar war tales (my favourite is *The Little Nations* in which armies of red and black ants enact the fighting at Gallipoli in the corner of an old clergyman's garden, which has strangely altered itself to resemble a map of the peninsula). Finally, in 1919, he celebrated the defeat of Germany with the story of *Drake's Drum*. Like *The Bowmen* it has been taken to be a real event; unlike that story, no one seems ever to have noticed, until I read the tale and recognised it as one with which I was already familiar from works on folklore. I subsequently wrote an article for the Winter 2006/7 edition of *Faunus*, the learned journal of the Friends of Arthur Machen, examining the legend of the drum and its growth over the centuries. It actually owes as much, if not more, to literary sources as to true folklore, and Machen's story was pivotal to its modern development. I think it is time he was given the credit.

So I am far from hostile to the idea of the castle legends deriving from literary sources. In fact, I look forward to my own stories, and others in this book, being repeated back to me as real experiences. But how convincing is Charles Kightly's statement that the White Lady originates in Edward Montague's 1806 novel? My first reaction was 'There has to be much more to the White Lady than that!' and my second was 'Surely that's the wrong date.'

According to Deryck Seymour (1), the first novel written about the castle was Mrs Bray's *Henry de Pomeroy* of 1841. He places Montague's work somewhere in the mid to late 19th century. I had never had any reason to question this, although when I first read Montague's book it did strike me as very dated in style for that time.

I took it down again, immediately after reading Charles Kightley's new guide, and re-examined it. I have the 1906 edition, published in Totnes by none other than A. E. and T. C. Mortimer. They were the proprietors, for the first fifty or so years of its life, of the *Totnes Times*, founded by their uncle in 1860. In their preface they say they first published the story 'long years ago' in a sister paper, the *Western Guardian*. This began in 1882. They issued the work in book form in 1892, and again in 1906. In the opening chapter there is a reference to a letter sent to the Mortimer brothers by the Duke of Somerset in 1875, which seems to prove that it couldn't date from before that time.

But then, as I skimmed again through the story, I realised that in the first few pages there are two distinct styles, and that most of the book would be extremely old-fashioned for the late 19th century. In diction it belongs much more to the beginning of the century, and the quotations used for chapter headings all fit the early Romantic period; no one would quote Ossian in the 1880s (except maybe Oscar Wilde). It began to look as if the Mortimers had merely added a few paragraphs at the beginning, with the sort of historical information that would not have been available to Montague. So perhaps it did date from 1806. I remembered a conversation in the pub a few weeks earlier with the writer Quentin S. Crisp, who told me that a small American publisher, of whom we were both aware, had reprinted the book in a series of 'Gothic classics.' I had never got around to checking this out, but a quick internet search explained all.

The Castle of Berry Pomeroy by Edward Montague was published in 1806, by William Lane's Minerva Press. Only two copies of that edition are known to exist: one in the British Library, the other in the Corvey Collection in

Germany. It was then published by the Mortimers in 1892 and 1906, and in 2007 was rescued again from oblivion by Valancourt Books, and is available from them as a high-quality, print-on-demand hardback. It can be yours for a mere £39.98. I was clearly right about the Mortimers just adding a few paragraphs near the beginning: when you read it carefully, the joins are obvious.

We'll examine the book's literary value (if that is the word) a little later, but does it provide the origin of the White Lady? The story concerns two sisters, Matilda and Eleanor (the Valancourt edition makes it 'Elinor'). 'The Lady Matilda,' we are told, is 'of a middling stature, elegantly formed; her mild blue eyes, sweet dimpling cheeks, the abode of the blushing rose.' She has 'coral lips' that when open display their 'ivory inmates,' and 'auburn hair falling in curls over her polished forehead.' Eleanor, who, interestingly, is a year younger, is 'of an unusually tall stature,' her 'beautiful dark brown ringlets' overshade her 'high forehead;' (what's this thing about foreheads?); she has 'animated dark eyes' and a 'majestic form.' Both sisters love the hero, a local knight called de Clifford, who loves Matilda. Eleanor, with the help of a corrupt priest, imprisons Matilda beneath the castle chapel, and announces her death. But Matilda manages to visit her lover as he weeps by what he believes to be her tomb. He thinks she is a ghost, and, rather than disabuse him, she merely tells him that they'll eventually be united in heaven. In the end it all works out, with Matilda and de Clifford married, the priest buried alive and Eleanor banished to a nunnery.

It looks, then, as if the story of the two sisters, one of them called Eleanor, does originate with Montague's novel (it is also, by the way, the likeliest reason for the Mortimers putting Eleanor in the tower in their guide; it was just a mistake, a faulty memory of the story they had once published, so we can forget about Celtic earth goddesses). But is it possible that the pallid figure of Matilda is the sole origin of the White Lady? I think it improbable. There is definitely more to her than that.

According to Deryck Seymour (2) people still encounter what can only be described as manifestations of the White Lady. They find the experience terrifying (which is probably why no-one leaves stuff for her in the tower; the story of the starved sister may be tragic, but this ghost is not to be placated by a bunch of flowers). Unless we dismiss them all as liars or deluded, we have to accept what they say. Matilda, in the novel, is never even described as walking along the ramparts, and you will remember that the 1867 quotation from *Bentley's Miscellany* mentions only a female ghost dressed in white, seen near the tower, with nothing about her being kept within it as a prisoner. The two themes had not yet come together, even then. If you're going to claim a literary origin for a traditional ghost story, the literary ghost and the 'traditional' one need to at least be doing the same thing in the same place. Then there's the tiny point that she's called Matilda, not Margaret.

And how influential was Montague's book, anyway? It seems to have died the death immediately after publication, and sunk into total oblivion (which is why there are only two known copies left). Until the Mortimers re-issued it, for a purely local market, it was dead to the world, though I suppose it is just possible that some of the early Romantic visitors to the castle had it with them when they were driven over from Torquay.

There is one other literary source I have not been able to look at, but that seems to provide another stage in the story's evolution. Deryck Seymour (1) refers to a poem in three cantos called *Berry Pomeroy* (1872) by Luke M. Combes, privately published in Torquay in two volumes. The plot is complicated, to say the least, but the relevant bit for us is that a Lady Margaret Pomeroy is imprisoned in a cell, and kept on the point of starvation, until rescued by her lover. She has not been locked up by her sister, though, but by the wicked Abbots of Buckfast and Torre, who covet her wealth for the church, and her prison is half way along an underground passage leading from the castle to Torre Abbey, which would be a most impressive feat of late medieval engineering.

Montague's novel and Combes's poem, between them, do seem to have provided the basic outline of the story of jealousy and imprisonment, although, as we have seen, the motif of a young woman in a dungeon was already in the air thanks to the name of the tower (where neither of these authors puts his heroine anyway); a confused folk-memory of St Margaret, long divorced from her religious context, as well as of the churching ritual, could just have lingered in the area, and contributed to the mixture.

So, rather than an ancient legend passed down unchanged from the time of the Pomeroys, we have a tale gradually evolving from many different elements: genuine sightings of ghostly female forms, a tower named after an imprisoned young woman, a totally obscure novel and an even obscurer poem (which only one or two people need to have actually read for their basic plots to be repeated and handed down), and the human tendency to alter and embellish a tale with each retelling, and eventually you have the story as I got it from S. M. Ellis's booklet in 1968.

Does any of this really matter? I happen to find it interesting for its own sake, but I believe the answer has to be yes. Just as it is valuable to realise that Dick Turpin was a vicious criminal, and not the romantic highwayman imagined by Ainsworth, so it is valuable to see just how complicated and varied are the elements that have gone into even such an apparently simple folktale about a fairly unimportant castle in Devon. Popular history programmes and the heritage industry present the past to us in straightforward, easily digested stories and images, while politicians, from parish councillors to presidents, constantly misuse and re-invent history to suit their own aims. But history is rarely simple and straightforward, and if our unpicking of even one small legend brings this home, then I think the exercise is highly worthwhile (Professor James Sharpe, in *Dick Turpin: the Myth of the English Highwayman*, to which I am indebted for the information about Ainsworth's *Rookwood*, puts this far more cogently than I can).

Many a Quaint and Curious Volume

The idea for a book of creative writings inspired by the castle arose from a conversation, in the Bay Horse Inn (yes, there are lots of weird continuities in this unfolding story), with the Ashprington author Laurence Green, whose collection, *Westcountry Stories of the Restless Dead* (Moorhen Publishing, 2008), includes a tale of the castle, featuring thinly disguised portraits of several local characters. He suggested an anthology of poems and stories, and I realised that I had been destined to put it together since that long-ago September afternoon in 1968. So now it is time to look at the responses of writers to the castle and its mysteries.

The only description we have of how Berry Pomeroy Castle looked before it became a ruin appears in *The Worthies of Devon* by the Reverend John Prince, vicar of Berry Pomeroy, published in 1701. Prince was born near Axminster in 1643. After studying at Oxford he was briefly a curate in Bideford, then became vicar of Totnes in 1675. Six years later the Seymours offered him the living of Berry Pomeroy, which then included Bridgetown. He spent the rest of his life here, dying in 1723.

His book has long been treasured by historians and genealogists as a valuable repository of local lore. Every Devon gentleman once kept a copy in his library, and when a suitor came to call upon his daughter, would look up the young man's ancestors in Prince. There was a second edition in 1810, and this is the one you'll find in reference libraries. It is typographically easier on the eye, but I prefer my folio first edition, with its esses looking like effs, even though reading it in bed can be awkward. It spent many years, before I acquired it, in the library of a Yorkshire gentleman, albeit one who had the taste to settle in Devon as soon as he could: Leonard Elmhirst, who, with his American wife Dorothy, did some interesting things at Dartington, most of which, sadly, have been undone by their successors.

Prince has traditionally been characterised as a touchingly voluble enthusiast for his native county and the great men it has produced. The impression Arthur H. Norway gives in *Highways and Byways in Devon and Cornwall* (1899) is typical: Prince is scholarly but complacent, constantly swelling up with pride at the thought of his good fortune in coming from such a supremely beautiful place. When I included him in my *Walks in the Totnes Countryside* (1995), I accepted this picture, and imagined him leading a quiet and contented life at the vicarage. I quoted his desire, through his book, to uplift and inspire, as he 'delighted not in weeding men's lives,' or 'throwing the nauseous trash upon their tombs.'

But his life was not all calm. Devon historians have long been aware of the scandal in Prince's career, but were unable to do anything with it until recently, because of the language in which the story is couched. But in 2001, in a little book called *The Curious Sexual Adventure of the Reverend John Prince* (The Mint Press, Exeter), Todd Gray weeded Prince's own life, and revealed everything.

On an April evening in 1699, the 52-year-old married parson, who was still a familiar figure in Totnes, was discovered by outraged townspeople trying to seduce a 29-year-old servant woman in a private room in a Fore Street tavern, not far from the Seven Stars. Crowds gathered to climb onto a bench and peer through the window, and to speculate as to whether or not the couple were having sex. Later they examined the floor, and found evidence to the effect that the vicar had perhaps not been completely successful in his aim... A local gentleman complained to the Bishop, and Prince was suspended for a year, only retaining his living through the intervention of his Seymour landlord.

So his book, which came out soon afterwards, is not the naïve, otherworldly celebration of famous men it has often been taken to be. There is a subtext of bitterness. He emphasises the greatness of the county's former inhabitants precisely because their descendants, his contemporaries, don't come up to the standards set by their ancestors: they will even sink to telling slanderous tales about a clergyman of the Church of England, for goodness' sake...

None of this, of course, makes any difference to the value of his description of Berry Pomeroy Castle, which appears in full in this book; the story is just a reminder that the self-righteous, 'tabloid' attitude towards other people's lives is nothing new. But before leaving the poor man in peace, I'd like to quote from his introduction, which he ends with the phrase 'from my study' (you'll have noticed I borrowed this for the acknowledgements), because I have always liked his definition of history:

> History is that which works Wonders; it recalls pass'd Ages and makes them present to us; and it opens us a way of conversing with the dead; without the danger of being affrighted with Mormos or spectres.

The question arises, though – is this just a conventional sentiment, or were Mormos (the ancient Greek word for monsters), and spectres, already a familiar part of life at Berry Pomeroy?

Next we come to the aforementioned 1806 novel by Edward Montague. Were it not about Berry Pomeroy Castle, it would not be worth spending very much time on at all. As it is, it could really be about anywhere, or at least any castle in a wood. It is almost a textbook example of how to write a fifth-rate Gothic novel using all the commonest elements of the genre, even down to the name 'Matilda' for the heroine, which was first used by Horace Walpole in the story that started the whole craze, *The Castle of Otranto* (1765). The book is extremely tedious, but I include a page or so from the beginning which, if you can tolerate his style for more than a few sentences, is quite effective: having set the scene, the author brings on the ghosts of the characters whose story he is about to tell; it reminds me of the opening of *Gormenghast*, where Peake similarly evokes those who died or disappeared in *Titus Groan*.

If you really want any more you'll have to search the world for a third copy of that rare first edition, seek out one of the Mortimer brothers' reprints (Totnes library has one in the reference section), or send your forty pounds to Valancourt Books, who obviously have a different opinion of its merits. But I suspect that what I give you here will be enough.

Our next description of the castle comes from a novel by one of those 19th century lady authors known to posterity as 'Mrs' somebody or other: Mrs Craik, Mrs Hemans, Mrs Oliphant and the rest (Elizabeth Gaskell used to be included, but her continuing importance has, thankfully, released her from this period usage). Our author is Mrs Bray, usually known as 'Mrs Bray of Tavistock,' just as the 17th century poet William Browne is invariably linked to that town.

She was born Anna Eliza Kempe in 1790 in London, though her ancestry was Cornish. She claimed that she originally wanted to be an actress, but that ill health prevented her (more likely it was family disapproval of a career virtually synonymous, at that time, with prostitution). In 1818 she married an artist and antiquarian, Charles Edward Stothard (1786–1821), who was working on a comprehensive project later published as *The Monumental Effigies of Great Britain*, but he died just three years later, falling from Bere Ferrers church as he sketched a window. It was then discovered that Stothard had stolen a small piece of the Bayeux Tapestry whilst making a study of it between 1816 and 1818. Unable to believe that a gentleman and scholar could be capable of such a crime, they tried to blame Anna, but it soon became clear that she was entirely innocent.

She married again in 1825. Her new husband, Edward Atkins Bray (1778–1857), the vicar of Tavistock, was a Dartmoor-born Romantic antiquarian, best remembered for his efforts to inscribe uplifting sentiments from the great poets onto the rocks of the Cowsic valley (see Philip Knowling's *Dartmoor Follies* for the story). Their marriage was happy and successful: they shared and supported each other's interests, and wandered and studied their beloved moor together for over thirty years, seeing everywhere the work of Druids and Phoenicians, to the amusement of later, more scholarly researchers.

Her most lasting work, still of value today, is a book that began as a series of letters in 1832 to her good friend the Poet Laureate, Robert Southey. These became *The Borders of the Tamar and Tavy: their natural history, manners, customs, superstitions, scenery, antiquities, eminent persons etc*. It was Southey who first encouraged her to write about her love for her locality, which is worth mentioning, because he has gone down in history for advising another young woman with literary ambitions, a clergyman's daughter from Yorkshire, not to bother (Charlotte Brontë, of course, ignored his guidance).

The word 'folklore' (originally 'folk-lore') had not even been invented when Mrs Bray started collecting it, but she is rightly remembered as a pioneer of the subject, and for students of Devon, especially of Dartmoor, she is as important as Baring-Gould, Rowe or Crossing.

But during her lifetime, Anna Eliza Bray was best known for her series of historical novels set in Devon and Cornwall, beginning in 1828 with *Fitz of Fitz-Ford*, the first Dartmoor novel. Others include *Trelawny of Trelawne* (1845) and *Courtney of Walreddon* (1846).

She typically begins these books by describing her visit to a place she has always wanted to see. Then she weaves a tale around the setting, often a confusing mixture of historical fact and romantic invention. This is certainly the case with *Henry de Pomeroy or the Eve of St John* (1841). She relates her visit to the castle in 1838, describing its appearance and what was understood of its history at that time, but then most of the novel is set elsewhere, in Tavistock and Cornwall. The plot concerns a late 12th century Sir Henry de Pomeroy who abducts the lady he loves from a convent, only to see her drown off St Michael's Mount. He also supports Prince John's rebellion against his brother, Richard I. The story reaches the castle right at the end, where it finishes dramatically. A royal herald arrives with a warrant for Sir Henry's arrest. He stabs the herald, then, realising that all is lost, he spurs his horse from the terrace to certain death in the valley below.

This ending may be the origin of the legend of 'Pomeroy's Leap,' the best-known castle story after that of the sisters. Or it may not: in S. M. Ellis's booklet the murder of the herald, and the leap, have become separate stories, and Sir Henry has become two brothers. But the story of the brothers seems to be older than Mrs Bray's novel: in an afterword she refers to a tale of the two last Pomeroys (relationship unspecified), throwing themselves over the cliff, which does suggest a prior legend. Some versions try to tie it all in with Sir Thomas Pomeroy's involvement in the Prayer Book Rebellion of 1549, complete with the king besieging the castle, but Sir Thomas had already sold the place to Sir Edward Seymour two years earlier, and the twelve-year-old Edward VI certainly did not lay siege to the latest item in his uncle's property portfolio (though Catherine Smith, ignoring historical reality, as I encouraged her to do, makes a beautifully rollicking ballad of the story later in this book).

Deryck Seymour (1), who always works on the assumption that the folklore came first, and that the novelists and poets simply made use of it, speculates that such a deeply-rooted tale must be based on a real incident, and suggests that it may have happened, centuries before the castle was built, during a battle between the local Saxons and the Vikings in 851. This, he thinks, took place just a few miles away, in the area around Weekaborough off the Totnes to Newton Abbot road. The story of a suicidal jump from a cliff might have been remembered locally and passed down as an oral tradition, later being transferred to the castle.

Henry de Pomeroy is not so hard to find in larger libraries, or antiquarian bookshops specialising in local work. Anna Eliza Bray lived to the ripe age of ninety-three, and was active to the end.

It has to be said that, though these descriptions are interesting, and often pleasing, nothing of real literary quality seems to have been written about the castle before the 20th century. Deryck Seymour (1) suggests that a poem by Elizabeth Barrett Browning, 'The Rhyme of the Duchess May,' written in 1844, might have been inspired by the legend of the Leap, but there is no evidence for this. However, there is a letter, from Tennyson, which contains more poetry and mystery in a few lines than anything we have yet looked at. Tennyson spent the May and June of 1848 on an extensive tour of Devon and Cornwall, during which he met Hawker of Morwenstow and saw the Arthurian sites that he used later in *Idylls of the King*. Tennyson scholars aren't even sure about the identity of the letter's recipient; it was obviously someone who had written to the poet on the lines of 'you probably won't remember me, but...' Whoever he was, we should be eternally grateful to him, because the reply conjures up a strange and unforgettable scene:

> You do me wrong by thinking that I have forgotten you and that pleasant day that we spent among the ruins of Berry Pomeroy. It was one of the golden days of my life. I remember it all – the voyage up the Dart, my meeting with you in the ruins, the lady who sat serving among the ivy, the little Theocritus which I had in my pocket, and even the rabbit we had to dinner. I did not know your name nor you mine.

Tennyson, his unknown acquaintance, the lady serving in the ivy (who was she, and *what* was she serving in the ivy?), and the rabbit, are now, for me, as much a part of the castle as Margaret and Eleanor (and unlike them, that day really happened; in fact, I'm almost convinced I was there). The 'little Theocritus' he had in his pocket was the volume of *Idylls*, by the Sicilian author of the 3rd century BCE, from which derived the whole genre of 'Pastoral' poetry, beloved of English writers in the 16th and 17th centuries: all those lyrical celebrations of shepherds and shepherdesses (not to mention the occasional nymph), making uninhibitedly bisexual love and disporting themselves in a semi-idealised landscape of 'sweet-cloth'd valleys,' mossy groves and crystal streams.

The Secret of Berry Pomeroy by Fred Wishaw, published in 1902, is a readable, boyish yarn, in the manner of R. L. Stevenson or John Meade Falkner, in which the ghost story of Pomeroy's Leap is elaborately re-enacted, on a regular basis, by a gang of smugglers, in order to keep people away from their nefarious activities. Wishaw uses the 'Two Brothers' version. The smugglers don't actually have two people riding over the cliff every time they perform the story, which would obviously be wasteful and counter-productive: they do that bit with sound effects, but then make a great show of loyal retainers retrieving the bodies and bringing them back up the steep path to the castle. Of Wishaw himself I can tell you only that he was also, according to the title page, the author of such splendid-sounding works as *The Lion-Cub*, *The White Witch*, *Clutterbuck's Treasure* and *The Three Scouts*.

In the early 20th century the best-known Devon author was probably the immensely prolific Eden Phillpotts (1862–1960). He is still worth reading: some of his Dartmoor novels approach greatness, and will always be of interest for the accuracy with which they depict the region's life in the late 19th and early 20th centuries; when I want to know how my hill-farming great-great-grandparents lived and spoke, I only have to read a few pages of Phillpotts. In 1903 he brought out a book of densely descriptive, leisurely essays, or prose meditations, called *My Devon Year* (Halsgrove republished it as recently as 2003), in which he ponders the mysteries of time, nature and the spirit of place. The one I re-read most often is called 'Granite and Sorrel,' where he contemplates an old ruined castle in the woods. He imagines a Norman knight surveying his new lands, his keen soldier's eye assessing the site for a stronghold, which soon rises in the silent forest; and how it is now gradually decaying into dust, while the tender wood-flowers endure. The fact that the castle he's writing about is neither Norman nor granite does not matter in the least.

Later, in *A West Country Sketch Book* (my copy has no date, but it says 'by the author of *My Devon Year*'), he visits the theme again in an essay called 'Berry Pomeroy,' ending, as night falls, down by the stew-ponds, as the wild ducks settle on the water.

Another early 20th century local author, with the same initials as Phillpotts, is not worth reading at all, but he has to be mentioned, as he did write about the castle. Elliott Plain is the name of a short street in Buckfastleigh. It was adopted as the pseudonym of the locally born Walter Holdsworth (1881–1947), for his novels and stories based on Devon folklore and traditions. As well as being very badly written, these books are interminably long-winded, and express a philosophy of unremitting gloom and futility: altogether a deadly combination. In one of his short story collections he has a tale called *The Crock of Gold*, which retells the castle legend about the two Totnes labourers who dream that such a treasure is buried beneath the large fireplace in the ruined mansion. They set out on a wild night to dig it up, but meet a local squire, who, on hearing of their mission, advises them to come back during the day when it will be safer. When they finally have an opportunity to do this, the treasure has already gone, and the squire has suddenly become much wealthier. Plain uses the story to demonstrate his conviction that life is pointless and any effort is doomed to failure.

I did think seriously about including it in this book, but in the end I felt I could not impose it on you, and anyway, I have no idea who owns the copyright to Plain's work.

Plain is actually such a hopeless writer that I decided, a few years ago, that he ought to be remembered, just for his persistence in the face of such minimal talent. I started the Elliott Plain Appreciation Society, by writing to various friends and telling them they were in it, and for over ten years now an increasing number of otherwise sensible people have gathered at Elliott Plain on his birthday, April 2nd, at 7pm, to sing an old song and pose for a commemorative photograph next to the street sign, before repairing to a pub, where we raise a glass to the memory of 'Devon's Worst Writer.' It has been described as a very 'British, enjoyable and silly event', and if your sense of humour is in any way tickled by the idea, you are welcome to join us.

In 1939 the novelist Elizabeth Goudge (1900–84) moved to Devon with her widowed mother. As soon as she arrived she felt, as many others have done, that she was not so much putting down roots as somehow finding roots already here. They lived in Marldon, in a wooden bungalow called 'The Ark,' later acquiring a plot in the Westerland valley, where they had a house built called 'Providence Cottage.' Goudge had enjoyed a modest following for her work, but in 1944 she experienced her first real success, when her novel *Green Dolphin Country*, set in the Channel islands and New Zealand, won an international award, was filmed and sold millions around the world. The taxman took most of her winnings, but this led to a public outcry, and eventually to a change in the law concerning literary prize money.

Elizabeth Goudge was born in Wells, Somerset. Her father was a clergyman and theologian. Her mother came from Guernsey, which features in her first novel, *Island Magic* (1934). When she was twelve the family moved to Ely, then Oxford, and small cathedral cities are favourite settings for her books, which tend to be gentle stories of modest characters quietly struggling to live good, spiritual lives in restrictive circumstances. All her novels have a strong sense of place. Their social attitudes may seem dated, but then, so are those of Henry James and Virginia Woolf. She can be sentimental and a touch whimsical, and her characters are as likely to 'ejaculate' something as to just 'say' it, but nobody's style is flawless. Over her long career she deepened both her vision and her expressive powers. Her seriousness of intent and life-long search for mystical understanding are evident from her autobiography, *The Joy of the Snow* (1970), which displays all her strengths and none of her weaknesses.

In this book she glowingly describes her life in Marldon, where she stayed until the end of the 1940s. Her love for the surrounding landscapes, which inspired several novels for adults and children, is evident. She remembers the steep-banked lanes, and a stile into a field from which she could look across to the blue outline of Dartmoor, and imagine generations of Devon people dreaming there, alone; she evokes the two nearby castles, one of them 'a haunted place hidden in the woods' (the other, of course, being Compton); a deep well in a lane, and a tree where a barn owl used to sit at twilight: all 'never to be forgotten,' as alive in her memory as 'human friends.'

Berry Pomeroy Castle appears in two, and possibly three novels. The most important is *The Castle on the Hill* (1942), in which it is the main setting.

It is not a ruin, but is still the home of the family who built it, though this changes by the end. The story takes place against the Battle of Britain and the blitz, bringing a disparate group of people to the landscape around the castle.

In *Gentian Hill* (1950), published after she left Devon for Oxfordshire, she celebrates her life in Marldon (which actually means 'gentian hill'), with a story set during the Napoleonic Wars. The castle features, but only briefly.

If, by the way, you find these books in 1970s paperback editions, do not let the cover designs put you off.

Her children's book *The Little White Horse* (1946) has achieved popularity in recent years through being televised as *Moonacre* and filmed in 2009 as *The Secret of Moonacre*. With J. K. Rowling's ringing endorsement, it is now safely enshrined as a children's classic. It includes a visit to a castle on a cliff in deep woods, and while not an exact description of Berry Pomeroy, it is reasonable to suppose that she had the place at least partly in mind.

While Elizabeth Goudge was dreaming her dreams in the fields and lanes around Marldon, a very different writer was working nearby, on the east bank of the Dart. Robert Graves (1895–1985), one of the great poets of the 20th century, had been living since 1929 in Majorca, until the Spanish Civil War forced him to leave. After some time in Europe and America, he spent the years of the Second World War in Britain, and a friend, the military historian Basil Liddell Hart, recommended the Totnes area. Graves lived at 'The Vales,' Galmpton, with his second family until 1946, when they returned to Majorca.

His was a complex personality. Although I have read a fair amount of his work, and about his life, I admit that I still have no clear sense of the man behind the severe, mask-like face, but I don't think I'm alone in this. Born in London, of cultured German and Irish parents, he went straight from an English public school (Charterhouse) to the horrors of the First World War, which I suppose would provide traumas enough for several lifetimes. Brought up with a repressed, prudish attitude towards sex, he developed a masochistic reverence for strong, dominant women, and in many of his books this is projected onto a highly individual interpretation of the ancient Goddess religions. He found lasting happiness with his second wife, but regularly tortured himself by falling hopelessly in love with a series of beautiful muses, though the torture resulted in poetry. His work seems extremely erudite, displaying what appears to be a profound knowledge of history, mythology, religion, ancient languages and anthropology, but he is often sparing in his citing of sources, or in giving detailed proof for his confident assertions.

His greatness is in his poetry, but he was a prolific author of prose books, many of them written to pay the bills, the best known being the 'Claudius' novels, his elucidation of the Greek myths and his war memoir, *Goodbye to All That* (1929). Then there's his strange and idiosyncratic study of poetic inspiration and Celtic mythology, *The White Goddess* (1948), written at the very time he was in South Devon. For Graves, the power of a poet's vision depended on his (and, apparently, it did have to be 'his'), cultivation and portrayal of The Goddess, the Muse, who often appears in ghost stories as a 'White Lady.' It is impossible to think that he did not, at least partially, have the White Lady of Berry Pomeroy in mind when he wrote this.

I knew, from Peter Underwood's *Guide to Ghosts and Haunted Places* (1996), that Graves visited the castle, and was driven away by an 'awful feeling of absolute terror' which he would 'never forget.' We should trust Underwood's account in this instance (it would be horrid not to), as he claims to have received it directly from Graves himself. I had already used this information in my story *Peril in Denim*, and I thought that was probably all there was to say, but then I had a hurried conversation, outside Totnes Museum, with Laurence Green, about a poem he believed might have been inspired by the castle. The date for that poem, which I knew, seemed incompatible with Graves's time in the area, but I decided to delve a little further. I contacted the Robert Graves Society, and they promptly came back to me with all the information I needed.

Another quick digression: biographers have to be selective, even American academic biographers, but an author's fan club is going to contain people who know, or aspire to know, absolutely everything, and will be eager to share this knowledge. So it is to them that you turn when you want the little details. It is necessary to be cautious, though; like anything else, literary societies can become addictive – I'm only in five, which is bad enough (for Machen, Hardy, Baring-Gould, M. R. James and Elliott Plain), but I know a couple of people who compete over the number they can set up.

There are two Graves poems relevant to Berry Pomeroy. The first, 'The Castle,' which is the one Laurence and I talked about outside the museum, can be found on page 303 of the Penguin *Collected Poems*. It is an intense, claustrophobic evocation of feeling besieged and unable to escape. Graves told the poet James Reeves that when he first went to Berry Pomeroy Castle, in September 1942, he recognised it as a place he had been dreaming about for years, and his experience there was that of the poem. He described it as his 'nightmare castle.'

Paradoxically, the poem was actually written in 1926 and probably owes as much to Harlech Castle in North Wales, which he had known since childhood, as it does to Berry Pomeroy, which he hadn't yet heard of, but as is the way with poems and dreams, the two places had blended in the deeper regions of his mind. Apparently Graves also wrote about the First World War before being in it, and one of his contentions in *The White Goddess* is that true poetic inspiration comes from a level of consciousness unrestricted by time, and is therefore able to encompass future as well as past experience.

'The Devil at Berry Pomeroy' (page 452 of the Penguin *Collected Poems*) is a strange, incantatory succession of disturbing, sometimes violent images, including witches calling for their imps, the birth of a two-headed monster, an ass being beaten to death, incest between a mother and son, and a weeping young woman leading an ape on a chain. It needs to be declaimed forcefully, and the castle is the obvious place at which to declaim it, but if you decide to go there and do this, I cannot be held responsible for any psychic or emotional consequences, which I suspect could be severe.

Graves refers to the castle and the origins of these poems in his last prose book, *The Crane Bag and Other Disputed Subjects* (1969), a miscellaneous collection of essays, articles and lectures. He was already, when he wrote them, sinking into the senility of his final years, and while some may find it interesting to have his opinion on the language of the *New English Bible*, or his views on the decline of bullfighting, it is not the most compelling of his works; when Totnes Library recently got me a copy from Exeter, I saw that I was the first person in Devon to borrow it for over eight years. So it is only really a book for the Graves completist. Or, of course, the Berry Pomeroy Castle completist – because what he says about the place is very interesting indeed.

It comes at the end of an article on reincarnation, which originally appeared in 1967 in that austerely intellectual publication, *Playboy* (you just never know where you're going to come across a reference to the castle; one of my own stories, *The Ghost-Watch*, which isn't in this book, was written in 2005 for an extremely improbable readership). The article is rambling and diffuse, and cannot have distracted its original readers from the rest of the magazine for very long, but a couple of pages, for us, are fascinating.

Graves describes how he went to the castle, found it closed, but managed to squeeze under the gate and into the courtyard. He was immediately overwhelmed by a 'nameless horror,' and the realisation that this was somehow the castle of his nightmares. Despite his feelings, he 'resolutely' explored the ruins, including the 'dungeons,' until he could 'stand the strain' no longer, and hurried away.

A couple of days later, a neighbour in Galmpton, Mr Beer, asked him if he had ever been to Berry Pomeroy Castle. On hearing that he had, Mr Beer gave him a photograph he had recently taken of the gatehouse. It showed what he said was a woman with a dog, who had not been there at the time. Graves examined the picture, and decided that the woman, who was 'tall and thin,' was wearing 14th century costume and leading a small ape, rather than a dog, on a chain. He found it so horrific that, once Mr Beer had left, he burnt it.

We may regret that a man who had survived four years at an English public school and then, immediately afterwards, another four in the trenches of Northern France, could not cope with a photograph of Berry Pomeroy Castle, but I suppose it testifies to the power of the place, and we cannot know what those years did to him: I was not being flippant when I suggested that his experiences would have provided traumas enough for several lifetimes. Or he may have burnt the picture because he just didn't want his very young children to be frightened by it. He states that his wife confirmed the presence of the woman with the chained ape, which became one of the images in the second poem.

Graves understood the image immediately, as a symbol of female sexual frustration. There is an Elizabethan phrase, 'to lead apes in hell.' Shakespeare uses it in *The Taming of the Shrew*, and 'hell' is one of his favourite euphemisms for the vagina. But Graves goes further, and suggests that the strange psychic disturbances at Berry Pomeroy are not caused by just any frustrated female sexuality, but the frustrated sexuality of an ex-queen.

He says that, long after leaving the area, he read that Isabella of France, widow of Edward II, had spent several years at the castle. Isabella had been 'leading apes in hell' for most of her married life, as her husband's sexual interests lay mainly elsewhere, and after his deposition she was kept in various places around the country, virtually as a prisoner, so that her lusts still remained unsatisfied. He reckoned that her deep frustration had imprinted itself onto the castle, where Mr Beer's photograph had somehow picked up this symbolic representation of it.

I'd love to know where Graves read all this, because, of course, it is impossible. Isabella lived from 1293 to 1358. There was no castle at Berry Pomeroy until long after that time, and there is no evidence that she ever came anywhere near the area.

Her life is well recorded. Edward II may or may not have been gay or bisexual, but Isabella had four children with him, so their relationship couldn't have been entirely devoid of affection, at least at the beginning. But he did not have the qualities deemed necessary for a medieval king, and in 1326, with her lover, Sir Roger Mortimer, Isabella led a rebellion against him. In 1327 they proclaimed her eldest son as Edward III. He was still a minor, and it was Mortimer's intention to reign for him. The young king put up with this for three years before dramatically claiming his birthright. Mortimer was quickly tried and executed, and though Isabella was briefly kept under house arrest, she was still the king's beloved mother, and he soon forgave her. She spent the rest of her life comfortably at court with her son and grandchildren, or at her various houses and castles, mainly around London, and certainly nowhere near Devon. There is just no space in her life for a prolonged exile to a remote corner of the kingdom with an obscure family of knights whose importance was exclusively local. She was a pious, cultivated woman, very different from the 'She-Wolf of France' of popular legend, a nickname she only acquired in the 19th century.

Ah, you might say, but she could still have visited the Pomeroys at the manor house in the village. Well yes, but it is unlikely, for reasons given above. She was a queen, and the Pomeroys were knights of the shire; there was a great social gulf between them. Anyway, the story of the family has been well told in another rare volume, *The House of de la Pomerai* (1947) by Edward B. Powley. From him, via Deryck Seymour (1), we learn that, for the period we're talking about, the manor was owned by two Sir Henry Pomeroys, the eighth and ninth of that name, who lived respectively from 1291 to 1367 and c1330 to 1373. The elder Sir Henry was certainly an important and wealthy landowner in the South West, but he had no connections at court and never attended parliament. His teenaged son experienced rather more action, as he accompanied Edward III on his 1346 invasion of France, and fought at Crécy. If either of them had been on visiting terms with the king's mother, Powley would certainly have known and recorded the fact.

So we cannot, alas, include Queen Isabella as an ingredient in the strange mixture that is the White Lady. I think Graves is right, though, to make explicit the psychosexual element to the experiences people have at Berry Pomeroy. This is a place, after all, to which generations of young people from Totnes, Torquay, Paignton and the surrounding areas have come, at night, with the deliberate intention of terrifying each other, and being terrified, out of their lives, amongst various other thrills. That is a lot of adolescent energy, and a lot of hormones, being focussed onto one place, inducing just the sort of state in which the interaction between mind and environment can produce strange visions and events.

I am not aware of any literary treatment of the castle since Graves's essay, until the writings of the various authors in this book, though I'm sure that if I have missed anything, I shall soon be put right.

The castle appears, however, in at least one film, and a brilliant short masterpiece it is: the Comic Strip's Enid Blyton parody, *Five Go Mad in Dorset* (1982), written by Peter Richardson and Pete Richens, directed by Bob Spiers, and starring a very youthful Dawn French and Jennifer Saunders as George and Ann. I don't know if any of it was filmed in Dorset, but it finishes beautifully; the children are suddenly in the Gatcombe valley, with the castle looming above, then in front of the gatehouse, and finally inside the castle, for a revelatory meeting with Uncle Quentin.

§

For the sake of completeness, I must mention two other ways in which the castle's name has been perpetuated. From the early Victorian period onwards, a journey between Totnes and Dartmouth by paddle steamer became an essential ingredient in a South Devon holiday. In 1880 a steamer called *Berry Castle* was launched at Kingswear, and she became the first in the long line of 'castles' that would be operated by the River Dart Steamboat Company for nearly a century. She plied the river until 1917. In 1921 the name was given to the company's first motor vessel, which worked until 1947; the third *Berry Castle* was in use from 1949 to 1972. I remember her well, as I do the smallest member of the fleet, the interestingly named *Seymour Castle* (1938–73).

Was it superstition that made them always avoid the full name, or did they just think it was too long to paint on the prows? Or was the 'Pomeroy' left out because they did not want to upset the Seymours, a powerful family in the area throughout the 19th and early 20th centuries? You will remember that the RAOB lodge at the Bay Horse did the same thing, and I can think of other instances from that time when it is referred to only as 'Berry Castle.'

The Great Western Railway had more courage, as in Totnes Museum you can see the name and number plates of the locomotive *Berry Pomeroy Castle* (50121), built in Swindon in 1927 to the design of George Jackson Churchward, who was born in Stoke Gabriel and educated at Totnes Grammar School. She was withdrawn from service in 1962.

§

When I invited authors to contribute to this book, I told them that, although the setting had to be recognisably the castle, they did not need to restrict themselves to the known history or folklore. I was delighted by the quality and variety of the material as it came in, and am pleased to present to you this fine collection of new works by some of my favourite local poets and short story writers, a couple from further afield, and others previously unknown to me. I feel privileged to be publishing such a talented company.

What comes across strongly from all the poems is the sheer power of the place's atmosphere. Some emphasise its air of sadness, others its mysterious and disquieting, even terrifying, power, which, as Peter Cowlam implies, can be worse than any horrors brought on by the most degraded urban addictions (though I trust he is writing from his imagination, rather than direct personal experience). I am also impressed by the range of poetic forms employed. Susan Taylor, Simon Williams, Pamela Sandry Gorman, Catherine Smith and Deborah Harvey draw quite specifically on history and legend, while Sue Hinds, Helen Ashley, Wendy Ruocco and Ken Taylor are more concerned with purely subjective reactions to the castle. The stories are all pleasingly different in style and approach. While Laurence Green and I are content to compose our own variations on a familiar tune, Anna Lunk takes it off in a new and very effective direction. Wendy Ruocco, Valerie Belsey, Debbie Miller-Wright and Idris W. Izzard just use the castle as a starting point for their own strange and beautiful journeys. I was not entirely surprised at how often Lady Margaret features in these poems and tales, though always in a way unique to each author. While I cannot guarantee that anything was actually written at the castle, some works may have been, and every writer has certainly captured an authentic aspect of its weird spell.

My own stories were written for friends at Christmas, to be read aloud in convivial company, like those of M. R. James and Robertson Davies, though whether they bear comparison with the tales of those masters, I shall leave to others to decide. My aim was simply to entertain for as long as it took to read or hear them. *The Story of a Vision and a Disappearance* was first read to a small but appreciative audience at the Bay Horse, by guttering candlelight, during a power cut in December 2010. Just as I reached the end, the lights came back on. Both tales have new endings, so don't skip them just because you think you know them already.

So now, in your imagination, come with me again to that turn-off to the left, on the winding road from Berry Pomeroy to Marldon, which is much busier now than it was in 1968. Climb the hill, looking back, as I could not do at the age of nine, over the rich landscape towards Totnes, and the southern edge of Dartmoor. Then go through the gateway between the cottages, and down the densely wooded drive. Blank out the industrial waste bins by the entrance, the security gates and notices and all the orange tape, and let yourself be enfolded by the woods as you move steadily downwards. Suddenly the castle is before you, brooding and aloof as ever. It is not beautiful. It is not, when you mentally compare it with other castles you may know, especially impressive in size or grandeur or military strength. It was never even properly finished. Nothing of historic importance ever took place here. The best-known stories about it are of people who never existed and events that never happened. And yet... even though we know all this, there is something strange, indefinable and unique about this place, which far greater castles, with real dungeons, in which terrible things really did happen, just have not got. I doubt whether people sit around in pubs or cafés talking about the castles at, for example, Middleham, Corfe, Caerphilley, Ludlow, Harlech, Arundel or Rochester (a completely arbitrary list, deliberately restricted to places I've never been to, but which I know have far more important historical associations), but mention Berry Pomeroy, in almost any social gathering, and you'll be talking about ghosts and weird experiences for at least half an hour (although if people do actually sit talking about those places, or any others, I'd love to know).

I think the 'something' is in the place itself, the ground and the rock underneath, rather than the buildings or anything that has ever happened in them. If the castle had never been built, I suspect that people would still have strange experiences in these woods, on this cliff-top and in the long valley below. Whatever the true origin or nature of this energy, the *genius loci* as it used to be called, it shows no sign of disappearing, but is as alive today as ever.

Deryck Seymour told me, in 1990, that he believed it was the ghosts that actually drove the family away: needing to live closer to London was just a convenient rationalisation, an excuse. I have been assured that this is an unnecessary hypothesis, and that there are already perfectly adequate reasons for their departure; but Deryck Seymour was no fool, and I take a perverse pleasure in entertaining the idea.

§

We have all had the experience of becoming completely absorbed in some creative activity, or piece of work, and then finding our environment strangely supportive, with pleasing synchronicities and serendipities providing us with whatever we need at exactly the right time. Writers find this especially encouraging whenever it happens, as it seems to suggest that all our solitary efforts are not, after all, a waste of time, and that we should keep going. Whilst researching and writing this introduction I have, as I hinted in the acknowledgements, had several such experiences. I shall end by sharing the one that impressed me the most.

The afternoon I was writing about the various early descriptions of the castle, I had just got to the point where I state that, interesting as they might be, there is nothing of real literary quality before the 20th century. I saved what I'd written, and went downstairs to make a cup of tea. While the kettle boiled I read a couple of pages of Peter Levi's biography of Tennyson, which I had recently picked up in a charity shop. I'd never taken much interest in Tennyson, and knew little about his movements. But suddenly there, on the page in front of me, was that strange and magical description of his day at the castle, ready to be included as soon as I resumed working. That's what I call support from the universe.

Further Reading

Most relevant volumes have already been mentioned during the course of this introduction. Berry Pomeroy Castle features in ghost books and local guides without number, but unless these are recent, and conscientiously researched, they often just copy the same material from each other. One of the best written is James Turner's *Ghosts in the South West* (1973). Marc Alexander's *Haunted Castles* (1974) mixes all the stories and legends together in an entertainingly imaginative, if highly misleading manner, emphasising the one that most authors make little of: the story of two lovers who, because a feud rages between their families, have to meet in secret. One day the girl's brother finds them, and immediately kills them to save what he sees as the family honour. This is, of course, an archetypal (and still contemporary) situation, with no specific connection to Berry Pomeroy Castle. Alexander tells what seems to me a very literary version, complete with names, but gives no sources other than S. M. Ellis. So I think he just made it up.

Most of the earlier castle guides can be found in local charity and second hand bookshops without too much difficulty. The one by the Mortimer brothers was on sale for many decades, and was reprinted frequently. It was not actually the first, though. That seems to have been a small book published in Torquay in 1858, entitled *History and Description of the ruins of Berry Pomeroy Castle, Devon*. It was issued and presumably written, by one Elliott, Printer and Bookseller, of Vaughan Parade. It doesn't really say very much, but it contains the descriptions of the castle by Prince and Bray, so I feel a pleasing sense of continuity with it.

The Mortimers' guide was finally replaced in 1947 by *Berry Pomeroy Castle: illustrated official guide* by Edward B. Powley, author of the Pomeroy family history referred to earlier. This continued to be reprinted until English Heritage took over. Deryck Seymour gives Powley an impressive list of academic qualifications, and I somehow always imagine him as a dark-coated antiquary out of an M. R. James story, carefully inspecting and measuring the ruins.

Then there is an orange-covered booklet just called *Berry Pomeroy Castle*, published in the late 70s or early 80s. There is no date, author or publisher, only the fact that it was printed in Callington, but I happen to know that it was written and published by Arthur L. Clamp, a prolific producer of guides and picture books for many years. As local author/publishers go, especially those of us in Devon, he was unusually self-effacing, so I welcome this opportunity to remind readers of his name. The photographs were clearly taken before the excavations and renovations began, so it shows the place pretty much as it was when I first saw it.

The first English Heritage guide appeared in 1990. It was by H. Gordon

Slade, and was the one that tried to deprive Margaret of her sainthood. This in turn was replaced by Stewart Brown's in 1997.

See J. V. Somers Cocks' *Devon Topographical Prints 1660–1870 – a catalogue and guide* (1977) for details of all the early illustrations of the castle.

The best general history of Devon is still W. G. Hoskins' *Devon* (1954), though Robin Stanes' *A History of Devon* (1986) should be nearby, as well as Helen Harris' *A Handbook of Devon Parishes* (2004), while Pevsner and Cherry's *The Buildings of England – Devon* (1989) is the essential guide to the built environment.

For the real story and character of Isabella of France, see Ian Mortimer's *The Greatest Traitor* (2003), and his excellent biography of Edward III, *The Perfect King* (2006), which will also tell you as much as you'll want to know about what the sixteen-year-old Henry Pomeroy saw and did in France in 1346.

The castle is a brief apparition in Richard Davenport-Hines' *Gothic – four hundred years of excess, horror, evil and ruin* (1998), a fascinating study of all that the word has meant in architecture, art, literature and life, though he is wrong in stating that the Protector Somerset himself had anything to do with the new mansion started by his son.

On the vexed question of hauntings, I recommend a book simply called *Ghosts* (2010), which is a lavishly produced, open-minded and comprehensive look at every possible aspect of the subject. It is by Jon Izzard who is also, under his real name of Ken Taylor, one of the contributors to this book (I break no confidentiality in sharing that information with you, as it is on his website).

Omnia Exeunt in Mysterium

From
The Worthies of Devon (1701)
John Prince

HAVING THUS DISPATCHED the arms and monuments belonging to this family [the Pomeroys], it may not prove ungrateful to give a brief account of the place of their ancient habitation. It was a castle, standing a mile distant towards the east from the Parish Church of Berry aforesaid. What it was in its antique form, can hardly be calculated from what at present remains standing; which is only the front, facing the south in a direct line, of about fifty cloth-yards in length. The gate standeth towards the west end of the front, over which, covered in moor-stone, is yet remaining Pomeroy's arms. It had heretofore a double portcullis, whose entrance is about twelve foot in height, and thirty foot in length; which gate is turreted and embattled, as are the walls yet standing, home to the east and thereof; where answereth, yet in being, a tower called St Margaret's, from which several gentlemen of this county anciently held their lands. Within this is a large quadrangle, at the north and east side whereof, the honourable family of Seymour (whose possession now it is) built a magnificent structure, at the charges, as fame relates it, upward of twenty thousand pounds, but never brought to perfection; for the west side of the quadrangle was never begun; what was finished may be thus described: before the door of the great hall was a noble walk, whose length was the breadth of the court, arch'd over with curiously carved free stone, supported, in the fore-part, by several stately pillars of the same stone of great dimensions, after the Corinthian order, standing on pedestals, having cornices or friezes finely wrought; behind which were placed in the wall several seats of frieze-stone also, cut into the form of an escallop-shell, in which the company, when aweary, might repose themselves.

The apartments within were very splendid; especially the dining room, which was adorn'd, besides paint, with statues and figures cut in alabaster, with admirable art and labour; but the chimney piece of polished marble, curiously engraven, was of great cost and value. Many other of the rooms were well adorned with moldings and fretwork; some of whose marble clavils were so delicately fine, that they would reflect an object true and lively from a great distance. In short, the number of the apartments of the whole may be collected hence, if report be true, that it was a good day's work for a servant but to open and shut the casements belonging to them. Notwithstanding which, 'tis now demolished, and all this glory lieth in the dust, buried in its own ruins; there being nothing standing but a few broken walls, which seem to mourn their own approaching funerals.

But what we may think strangest of all is, that one and the same age saw the rise and fall of this noble structure!

From The Castle of Berry Pomeroy (1806)

Edward Montague

'Often are the steps of the dead in the dark eddying of blasts, when the moon, a dull shield from the east, is rolling along the sky.'

Ossian

IN THE WEST of England are yet to be seen the ruins of Berry Pomeroy Castle, formerly a place of great strength, but now, like its proud ancient possessors, almost forgotten, and daily mingling with the dust.

Many are the dark deeds said to have been perpetrated within its walls, as the yet bloodstained stones and flitting shades that nightly hover over their sad remains, entombed amongst the ruins or buried without sepulchral rites, are sad mementos of. Often do their wailing shrieks vex the nocturnal breeze, that else would sleep in quiet amidst the shady branches of the surrounding woods.

But more horrible than all, dwell on the affrighted air the dreadful groans of the blood-stained Sir Ethelred de Fortebrand, cut off by the just decree of an avenging Power, in the prime of his years, by the keen dart of the assassin.

Soon as the vapours of the night condense upon the earth, appears his melancholy form wandering amidst the ruins, under whose cumbrous weight, in the silent vaults beneath the chapel, are his murdered remains.

Close by his side, condemned for ever to wander on the earth, restless and miserable, stalks the shade of the guilty Lady Eleanor de Fortebrand: and when the gale brings on its broad pinions the hollow sounds of the distant Abbey clock of Ford, when it tolls for midnight prayer, then do the furies arise, armed with writhing serpents, whose death-darting tongues glisten with poisonous venom, and whose pestiferous breath instantly blasts each herb and flower: with these they lash with horrible yells the shrieking shade of the Lady Eleanor, and then lay her beside the murdered Sir Ethelred, on sharp quick-piercing brambles.

Thus is her guilty spirit condemned to endless tortures, the due punishment for her horrible deeds. Silent, solitary, and restless, glides among the hanging woods the pale ghastly form of the Abbot Bertrand, the cruel and deadly instrument of the Lady Eleanor de Fortebrand, cut off, when he least expected it, by a most horrible death, the just reward of his atrocious actions.

Such are the reports which the neighbouring peasantry have handed down to their offspring, and who, to this day, relate to the traveller.

> *Here, in their two editions, the Mortimer brothers incongruously insert over two pages of historical information concerning the castle, which could easily have been placed in a separate introduction, before allowing Montague to continue.*

Strange and horrible it is to tell, that these ruins, so fitted to calm contending passions, and convey a soothing serenity to the mind, should have been the spot where foul murder, hatred and envy, deceit, and every base passion of the mind, instigated by the fell demons of darkness, held their dread abode.

From Henry de Pomeroy,
or The Eve of St John (1841)
Anna Eliza Bray

I HAD LONG entertained the wish to visit that part of Devon known by the name of the South Hams; but not so designated, I presume, as an ingenious historian once conjectured, in honour of Ammon, who, he states, was worshipped by the Druid priesthood on the southern coast of that county; for as the word Ham was anciently applied to a low pasture ground, situated near a river or the sea, this circumstance alone seems to point out the source whence the Hams derived their name, as the cattle ground of Devon...

But no longer to digress, I shall commence at once with noticing that part of our journey which gave rise to the following work, our visit to the very ancient and very interesting ruins of the Castle of Berry Pomeroy, near Totnes, in Devonshire.

My companion had visited it many years before, but now scarcely recognised it again, so much was it altered by the course of time. To me it was all new ground; and my impressions, therefore, were perhaps more lively than his on this occasion. It do not wonder that he found some difficulty in recognising an old acquaintance here, for the very gateway of the castle was so hidden by trees, and so overgrown with ivy, that, on a first approach, it is no easy matter to make out what it is.

We had left the carriage in which we drove to the spot; and a little girl, who told us she was ten years old, had accompanied us from a cottage near the entrance of the wood, with the keys of the castle; under her guidance, we were now to proceed to the inspection of the ruins.

Passing under the gateway, we ascended to what is generally called the chapel; but which was evidently the guard-room, above the entrance, as the opening for the fall of the portcullis still remains in the walls. Here are three arches supported on rough columns, of a very ancient appearance. The flanking towers of the gateway lead to the ramparts; and all this part of the building, I am convinced, is of high antiquity: most likely the work of that De Pomeroy on whom the manor was bestowed by William the Conqueror, and who was the original founder of this once stupendous castle...

After a careful survey of the whole, we could not help saying that Berry Pomeroy would be a most interesting ruin, if it were not so encumbered with brambles and trees, as in many places you can see nothing else. That portion of the castle which is stationed on the esplanade, above a rocky precipice at the back of the building, is so completely surrounded by trees that you are scarcely conscious you are near a precipice till on its very verge. Indeed, at this spot only heaps of rubbish indicate the foundations of exterior walls, long since fallen into ruin, and the castle is so much injured and dilapidated along the whole range of the esplanade, that only fragments of four lofty towers remain. Here, therefore, the ruin is most complete...

The castle, as I have noticed, was evidently built at different periods, and should it continue a few years longer, the confusion to the tyro antiquary will be greater than it is already; as, for the purpose of strengthening the building, and also for securing it against the inspection of gratuitous visitors, walls with rude embattlements have recently been built from one part of the structure to another, giving it a patchwork appearance, very incompatible with picturesque beauty...

By a winding path through the wood, we descended the hill, at the foot of which runs a little brook: this, collected into a pond, turns a mill, that, no doubt, belonged to the castle; as (after scrambling up the opposite bank, whence we had a somewhat less obstructed view of the ruins), when we reached the summit, we found the mill was built with some share of ancient architectural ornament. Soon after seeing this, we bade adieu to Berry Pomeroy.

Berry Pomeroy
Deborah Harvey

This castle bristles with ghosts.
There are Ladies of varying hue: Blue, White.
A sister starved in a tower by her sister
in rivalry over a lover,
a daughter who smothered her inbred,
tormented by its cry, and other
indeterminate shades
fray at the edges of my eye. True,

time pools in this deep cleft
amid the sickly meadowsweet,
purple loosestrife burning
like an accusation,
but I have come here to lay phantoms,
not to raise them,
my spirit cut down from its gibbet
above this broken hill,

moribund but breathing,
breathing still.

Remains
Helen Ashley

Walls within walls, mansion within castle, erected
for Pomeroy defence, for Seymour domesticity.
Tried by the one, found wanting by the other.
Three centuries' disintegration opened them
to all that the weather would throw,
neither offers sanctuary or shelter now.

Lightning, thunder: flash, clatter, rumble
last leap of horses and men from ramparts' height,
final breath roared from fall to valley depth.

Storm wind wails through crumbling walls:
starved sister, daughter defiled, infants torn
from life before childhood claimed them.

Clouds fold and unfold a moonlit sky:
white light and midnight blue stroke battlements,
mould and manifest shadow to woman-form.

Rain washes space between stone, and stone itself,
gathers tears, filters grief through troubled earth,
adds history's weight to the waters of Gatcombe Brook.

Walls within walls, Berry Pomeroy Castle is all
unpeopled now but for those whose visit is brief,
whose feet may tread only twenty-first century deep
but whose thoughts make what they will
of something, that could have been sound or sight
or a hand that touched, or might have done.

Ellie and Mags
Laurence Green

WHAT I AM about to tell you defies all logic and worries me to this day, even though it only happened last year. I really should not tell you this story, because it calls into question my credibility as a teacher and as a reasonably sane human being.

My name is Alan Brown and I have taught English and History at King Edward VI Community College in Totnes for a number of years. I am form tutor to 7 Churchward 2, and particularly enjoy the pastoral part of my job, helping young people to grow up and to acquire the study skills necessary to see them through GCSEs and beyond.

The new Year 7 curriculum is an exciting one, integrating humanity and science subjects to develop lively minds, at least in theory! I had a hand in writing the History and English project based on Berry Pomeroy Castle. As a result I presided over the forthcoming visit to the castle and the preparatory lessons preceding it.

We studied the history of the castle; why it was built, when it was built and what happened when the Norman de Pomerais handed it over to the Seymours. We studied the transition from fortress to mansion, from defensive to domestic architecture. We shuddered at the eerie legends that persist to this day concerning both the Seymour and de Pomerai families.

At last the day came for the visit to Berry Pomeroy Castle. My form and I gathered in the form room with drinks and sandwiches, waterproof anoraks, clipboards with pen, pencil and paper and money for ice creams at the Castle café, all the things important to twelve-year-old students. I had first aid kit, epi pens, mobile phone, medical details of students with special needs, and all necessary permission slips. While I waited for the two Teaching Assistants and Mrs Albertson to come across the road I took the register:

'Put that drink away please Tamsin. Quiet please everyone. Answer your names clearly please. Don't say anything if you're not here.

'Sally Atkins… Jordon Pearce…. Simon Pengelly… Ellie Pomeroy… Mags Pomeroy…'

While we waited for a few students to go to the loo I considered the Pomeroy twins. They were old fashioned in the best sense, devoted to each other in a way that only twins could be. They lived on a farm near the village of Berry Pomeroy and must have known all about the castle. They were always attentive and well behaved, asking intelligent questions about the history and legends with no sense of condescension or superiority. They were good sports, who looked after each other and always watched out for each other, as if it were their second nature to do so. They were very pretty in an innocent way, and altogether good and conscientious students.

We made the short journey to the castle in the two battered school minibuses. Soon we made the sharp turn from the narrow lane, past the three cottages, and down the winding wooded hill to the clearing where the castle stood on its crag surrounded by ancient beech and newer larch trees. We were suddenly in a remote world with Totnes miles away and the past a tangible entity.

The students were strangely quiet as they got out of the minibuses and looked at the tall trees with a gentle breeze touching their tops. We sat on the wide sun-dappled lawn facing the curtain walls with their ramparts, the twin towers of the gatehouse and the high ruins of the Tudor mansion which seemed to frown from behind the walls.

'Listen up, everyone. Make sure that you remain in your group of four, and be aware that there are steep drops into the valley on the far side of the castle. You are here to do three things in any order you like. Draw a rough diagram of the castle, pacing out distances, and label it; draw a careful sketch of any part of the castle that appeals most to you, and write a short story based on any aspect of the history of the castle that you like. Do not climb on the walls or raise your voices at any time. Do not run or drop any litter. The loos are behind the café. Ask any of us if you have any questions. Remember that there is no such thing as a silly question if you really want to know the answer.'

'And if you see the ghost of Lady Margaret, ask her if you may help her,' I added to Annie the Teaching Assistant, a remark I later had cause to regret.

I presented the educational group pass to the English Heritage curator and we entered the castle together, an orderly group slightly overawed by our surroundings. I think that it was the remoteness that has this effect on us. That and the contrast to the former bustle of the busy classroom a handful of miles away.

The inner courtyard of the castle was a bumpy grass area surrounded by high walls on two sides, the ruined mansion on the third and ragged pillars of stone on the side overlooking the steep valley. According to legend, the Roundhead bombardment had all but destroyed the castle walls and the mansion range that led from the kitchens to the great hall in the main block.

We split into groups; some to explore the ramparts and chapel in the gatehouse, some to look at the massive kitchen block with its huge fireplaces now open to the sky, and some to wander around the rooms and courtyard of the roofless mansion ruin, whose granite window frames rose high overhead.

Excited voices could be heard arguing about this and that, but all the students were hard at work completing their assignments. Soon it was time for Annie and I to go to the café outside the castle. We sat in the sun facing the twin towers of the gatehouse, the high ramparts and the remote round tower at their right hand end.

'That's funny,' said Annie. 'I could swear that there is glass in the windows of the round tower. There certainly wasn't a moment ago.'

I looked at the roofless tower beyond the lawn where the moat used to be. Sure enough, I could make out the shimmer of diamond panes contained within the granite window frames.

Then I heard the first voice raised in anger floating shrilly across the lawn.

'I know you fancy him Mags! You can't deny it, you little bitch! But I love Tom much more than you ever will…'

A loud shriek sent us both running towards the gatehouse and along the rampart walk to the tower. There stood the lone figure of Ellie in great distress, tears running down her pale face. She was sobbing so hard that she could hardly speak, and shaking uncontrollably. Finally she turned to me and sank down onto the stone floor of the round tower room. Mutely she pointed to the head of the spiral stone staircase that turned out of sight to the darkness below.

'I don't know what came over me. I… I pushed her. Down there. I heard her fall. I don't know what we're going to do…'

Her eyes rolled up into her head as she passed out on the cool floor of the tower room. I looked at Annie with a growing realisation of what had happened.

'Phone for an ambulance as soon as you can, and look after Ellie. I must go down there,' I said in a shocked voice.

With a heavy heart I set off down the slippery stone steps into the dungeon-like ground floor room of the tower. I expected at every turn to see a sprawling smashed body with limbs twisted at crazy angles and blood everywhere.

I was almost more shocked to find an empty round room with a small fireplace and a smell of damp earth. Of Mags Pomeroy there was no sign, no trace at all.

I knew that Ellie had pushed her, but where on earth was her beloved sister? I searched all over the castle and organised groups to look for her. I alerted the custodian who looked in all the hiding places known to her. Finally I phoned the police and notified the school. We were utterly mystified; there was no place for 'vanished off the face of the earth', despite *Picnic at Hanging Rock*, on the risk assessment form we had so carefully filled in as part of our thorough preparations for the visit.

Ellie had regained consciousness and was taken away in an ambulance. She had not said a word and seemed to be in deep shock, eyes staring from the palest of faces. Groups of her friends stood tearfully together as the ambulance drove carefully away. A stunned silence prevailed. No one wanted to look directly at anyone else.

No sign of Mags was ever found. The search for her grew: the ponds near the castle were dragged, lines of searchers walked slowly through the woods and over the hills, all road and rail links in and out of Devon were examined. Reports of sightings came from as far away as Perth and Penzance but no trace of the little girl was ever found. The nation-wide search spread abroad, but foundered in a fog of supposition.

The Pomeroy family were left to grieve in private. I was offered counselling but turned it down on the grounds that I certainly could have done nothing in my power to prevent the tragic disappearance of Mags. Ellie eventually recovered, but would never talk about what had happened. Her mind had mercifully blanked out the mysterious events of the day her twin sister vanished.

That is not the end of the story, however. A few months after our summer visit to the castle something very strange happened. Tom, the Pomeroy's cowman, who had only recently left school in Totnes, was badly injured when his motorbike swerved suddenly into a tree in the lane close to the entrance to Berry Pomeroy Castle.

During the long recovery process in Torbay Hospital he was interviewed several times by the police. His story never changed: there were no traces of drugs or alcohol in what had been left of his blood before massive transfusions set him on the path to eventual recovery.

He was a good lad, a careful worker and a very good employee. He said that as he was driving home after work, past the castle entrance, a young girl stepped out of the hedge directly in front of his bike. He had no time to stop, and passed right through her. There was no impact and he clearly remembered the girl's face before he hit her and swerved into the tree.

'It was Mags. Of that I am absolutely certain, cross my heart. But she was no living girl. Her face held no expression. It could not have been Ellie because, after her recovery, she had been taken out of school in Totnes and sent to a girls' boarding school in Newton Abbot. And no, I was not aware that either girl had a crush on me. Had I been so I would certainly not have encouraged it. I am totally mystified by the whole business...'

Guardroom,
Berry Pomeroy Castle
Simon Williams

On the wall behind the oratory screen,
over from the bare rock hearth,
are oxidised maroons and powder blues
with faces reduced to pen cartoons.
Mary, in precarious shippon,
has visitors in medieval gowns,
one black face in the Flemish manner,
come to see a Jesus, faded near to plaster white.

Stand here for any time and two swallows
swoop to visit through the open door,
circle, veer in insect-lock trajectories,
as if we're in some freeform aviary.
They settle high along the roof truss,
feed young, already stretching wings;
black, white, with a single flash of blood-rust,
soon to take their gifts to Africa.

The Lost Moat
Sue Hinds

The ground Floor is accessible with care,
lime mortar spared in the dungeons of despair.
What on earth made you want to go there?
where spiral staircases reel out of repair?
The walls of time sink into the virgin soil,
there my lover came to me
with a glassy glaze to spoil.
I drank the draft and it set me free.
As the summer fell in the gatehouse chamber
The red, red droplets like wine
became patterned in the autumnal amber
that made my bright eyes shine.
There below lay the deep dark moat
The deed is done
There's no need to gloat
As the shadows flitter over what's left of the sun.

A Spirit Journey
Ken Taylor

Emptiness.

> A shell,
> broken
> and hollow.

In our watching, we fill its void with our presence.
> Yet the question still flutters in the shadows:
> did
> life break free,
> or did
> death break in?

Here, where life once was,
> seeping decay dissolves even the stones
> whose quantum memory enshrined the force
> of all past events.

But time turned its back on Berry Pomeroy Castle,
> once jubilant, colourful, and bold.

Ruin has dominion.

> The eggshell walls of its halls are the haunt of bats;
> its flagstones resound only with the scratching claws
> of nocturnal creatures,
> its solitary guests
> until daylight brings
> the return of the curious,

questing tourists…

Visitors feast on a banquet of matured and savoury deceits
     still succulent with wrongs un-righted,
     richly glazed with vanity,
     and garnished with the tang of stricken nobility.

Vampires suck the residue of warrior blood
     slaughtered by the reversal of bright fortunes
     that rose only to be crushed.

Voyeurs glut on the romance of glory turned decadent
     in tragedy's triumph over the innocent heart.

     And, all the while, tendrils of green chaos
       creep quietly closer,
       smothering secrets
         to reclaim the site of their banishment.
     Exiled no longer, the resurgent greenwood infiltrates
      with invisible stealth and calm inevitability.

     The annual ebb and flow of regeneration
      sets the scene for living theatre.

Ghosts flock from the wings
     hurling thoughts, moods and the seeds of dreams
     into the open hearts of wide-eyed vigil-keepers.

Here the eternal battle is waged between endings
     and beginnings.

Lovers come to find each other,
     and leave knowing more
      than they ever thought possible.

Visionaries delighting in the esoteric or macabre
     find themselves seduced to linger and return

time and again
until a final inspiration satisfies their quest,
    illuminating their entire journey
        from inception to end.

Here, the quest for forbidden insight may lay bare a truth
    so wondrous that words shrivel —
        such mysteries perish
          amid pale repetition,
        and must be won
          by a valiant conjured rebirth
        from an instant
          made pregnant with selfless love.

Treasures lying here may buy the means to bury the heart
    in a coffin of gold,
or set free the insurmountable laugh
    that heals the world
    to bathe blithely
    in the light of the long-dead suns
    that shine upon all by day
        as well as by night.

And always with us here in this castle of black forms,
    are the shrieking voices of spirits
    still communing half-unremembered
        hopes and fears
    whose echoing meanings fill a maze
    of branching possibilities
        that few dare divine.

All around this paranormal maelstrom
    where wonders ride naked
    in the glimmering
        on the brink of consciousness —

all around this pinnacle of unimaginable opportunity

where moments tangle in flickering visions
      surrounded by pure white light –

all around us now
      we may hear the song of that limitless liberty
      into whose embrace we may yet slide –

    as we finally leave this riotous place
      to resume our lives.
      Even as we tremble to the end
        of this journey,
        we find ourselves waiting
          to clothe our experience
          in embroidered purpose
            resplendent
            enriched
              and radiant.

The Mason's Mark
Valerie Belsey

'Before the door of the Great Hall was a noble walk, whose length was the breadth of the court arched over with curiously carved freestone and supported in the forepart by several stately pillars of the same stone of great dimensions.'

John Prince, 1701, vicar of Berry Pomeroy for twenty years

'TAKE ME THROUGH that again Mr Franklin.'

The merchant, a sickly looking skinny man, constantly wringing his hands, stood in his dusty shoes as he was quizzed by Sir Edward Seymour's Steward. The Steward eyed him up and down and wondered how he always managed to get through the gatehouse without being taken for a serf. Still, he was well-loved by Sir Edward, and so now he must be dealt with as he sat tearing gobbets of flesh from a side of pork in front of him on the kitchen table. The Steward started to repeat himself.

'The columns are not complete because Sir Edward has run out of...'

Franklin interrupted eagerly, a cajoling look of triumph in his eye.

'Money?'

The Steward, slightly annoyed, continued: 'Oh no, money, that's not the problem, it's the Beer stone, it comes up the Dart you see but dragging it up over the hills and levering it over those old walls, well, sometimes there's very little left for the masons to carve with, and they can be difficult those masons. Sir Edward would give anything to see the colonnade, the loggia, finished.'

The merchant reached for the wine.

'Anything, you say, well. I'll see what I can come up with. Can I see Sir Edward now?'

He pushed his pewter platter forward.

'Thank you, I've eaten enough.'

He stood up and walked through into the loggia leaving behind the clatter and bustle of the kitchen. So what did the Steward mean? On seeing one of the serving girls bent over one of the scallop alcove seats, he slunk back behind a half erected column. She gracefully flicked her thick black hair behind her ears and, with slim, but calloused, fingers traced something incised in the back of the recess. She caressed the pattern over and over again. Franklin saw that this was a loving caress, one which he wouldn't have minded receiving himself. Startled by the crunch of his footstep she shot upright to face him as he came forward, then lowered her gaze and bowed.

'Girl, stop, what are you doing here? Servants aren't allowed in this loggia.'

She stared wide-eyed, startlingly blue-eyed, he thought, and she had understood his use of an Italian word.

'This passage, I mean. Loggia, that's an Italian word.'

'I knows zur, it's Italian.' She replied, in a soft local accent.

'You know Italian, a servant girl who walks in her master's footsteps and yet knows Italian words. What were you doing, poring over those seats?'

'Clean 'un up zur.'

'Mm,' he muttered.

'I'll say nothing to the Steward. What's your name?'

'Tamsin Steer, zur.'

'Well, get back to where you belong, mistress Steer.'

He blocked her way through so that he caught the fragrance of lavender and mutton fat on her hair as she squeezed by, whispering an unwelcome 'I shan't forget you,' into her ear, and adding, 'or what I saw you doing.'

He made his way along to the seat and to the part of it which Tamsin had been 'cleaning'. There, set amidst straight-lined mason's marks, was what looked like a fish but, when drawing away from it, it seemed more like a round object about to take to the skies. He too ran his fingers over the image. He knew that there were nearly thirty masons under the direction of William Arnold master mason, and that this was the sign of one of them. Yet this seemed more like the work of an ethereal carver, not from these shores, he thought.

'Ah Franklin, they told me you were in the kitchens. Still, here you are now and look, you can see what the problem is.'

Sir Edward suddenly appeared from the North Wing and unrolled a plan in front of Franklin.

'Signor Serlio Sebastiano laid out these plans, but the masons that Arnold employs are rough locals, stone-breakers really.'

'Greetings Sir Edward. Locals you say, but surely not all of them; there is the work of a fine hand here.'

'Yes, Franklin you're right, there has been a fine hand here, an Italian one, but he's gone, and I don't know how to get him back. Anyway, what brings you here today?'

Franklin quickly understood where the anxieties of his employer concerning the Italian lay and, for a second, delayed in his reply as the image of Tamsin caressing the seat came to him again. Sir Edward waited in a haze of smoke as he puffed and pampered his pipe; he was forever grateful for that merchant venturer from East Devon for bringing the habit to him. Also he was thankful that the smoke kept the midges and flies away, which swarmed in the morass below as he paced and fretted over his unfinished loggia.

'Well,' Franklin began. 'I see that in the kitchens your stock of Chinese porcelain is down.'

'Yes, down on the floor, clumsy local oafs, my biggest best dish shattered, only yesterday.' He doubled his pipe-puffing rate. 'It's not just Italian masons I'm missing but Chinese porcelain too, so how can you help?'

'I can suggest a solution for the loggia at least, sire.'

'Well, what is it?'

'I can't say yet, it's something I'm working on. But there is another stock of Chinese porcelain I know of.'

'Too expensive I expect, like the Italian masons.' Sir Edward placed himself firmly at the centre of his loggia like an actor and said 'Too expensive I expect, like the Italian loggia mason. I must choose one or the other.'

§

SOLANIO Now what news on the Rialto?

SALARINO Why, yet it lives unchecked, that Antonio hath a ship of rich lading wrecked on the narrow seas; the Goodwins I think they call the place; a very dangerous flat and fatal where the carcasses of many a tall ship lie buried, as they say, if my gossip be an honest woman of her word.

William Shakespeare, *The Merchant of Venice*, c1597, Act One, Scene One

Six Months Later

'Well read, my boy, well read,' Sir Edward shouted, slapping his son Edward on the back as he read from the manuscript, pacing up and down the loggia as he went.

'We'll have a full performance of one of her Majesty's favourites, that Mr Shakespeare, and we'll have it here when our loggia is complete, eh Franklin?' He added in hushed tones, 'And in front of her Majesty.'

The merchant stood to one side to let his employer parade as he needed. How prophetic were the words of the poet, he thought, knowing as he did that Sir Edward had recently come into a fortune from some ship which had floundered on the coast, and it was his job to oversee 'the fate' of the cargo. He hoped that it had been enough to make his dreams come true.

'Right Franklin, that choice we spoke of a while back doesn't matter now. Where's the porcelain you spoke of? I'll have more, and the Italian mason, bring him back, I can pay him now.'

If Franklin had been a pipe smoker he would have, at this moment, obscured the loggia with wreaths of tobacco smoke like celebratory banners. During the six months that had passed he had pursued the maid, Tamsin, with promises of returning her Italian lover to her at the castle: if she would only tell him where he was, he would bring him back. She told him that he was working on Exeter Cathedral. Franklin arranged a secret meeting place for the lovers but that first meeting did not involve the third party she had been expecting to meet. Tamsin was forced to agree to Franklin's personal demands. He promised her that the next time she would see her Italian lover.

Lorenzo, from Florence, was eager to return to the idyllic, erratically paid life at Berry Castle and the charms of Tamsin. After some prolonged negotiations with the Exeter masons Franklin had him freed. He set sail for Dartmouth and caught a ship up to Totnes on the Dart.

'No, no wait.' Sir Edward stopped in his perambulations.

'I'll not have that porcelain until I see the mason from Italy here. Can you bring him here to me tomorrow? I want the young man who has worked with Signor Serlio Sebastiano here to work this Beer stone as it deserves. Where is he? This North Wing of mine will be the greatest, the grandest, in the West, in the whole of the kingdom.'

§

And so Lorenzo and Tamsin were re-united and Sir Edward was happy for a while as long as the merchant venturer's money kept coming in. Franklin was happy with his double payment. However, one stormy, wet evening Tamsin, heavily pregnant, tripped and dropped another one of Sir Edward's favourite Chinese dishes onto the flagstones in the Hall. It is said that the pattern the potshards formed upon the floor resembled Lorenzo's mason's mark. This angered Sir Edward even more. Yes, the mason was good, but he worked so slowly that his money was running out again. What was the use of a loggia when the rooms around were still unfinished and he wanted the Hall completed for Good Queen Bess to come and stay and see it herself?

Well, as you see – it never was – and she never did.

§

As for Tamsin and Lorenzo, they fled from Sir Edward's tetchiness and stifling wreaths of tobacco smoke. Oddly enough they settled in a secret location over in Raleigh country in East Devon. They had many children, all having dark, Mediterranean complexions; all, that is, with the exception of their firstborn. On hearing of the death of his old master in 1613, and of how a monument was being carved showing him reclining with all his children, a similar number to his own, around him, Lorenzo decided to return for a while. He came back to Berry to give thanks for the happy times he had spent at the troubled court of Berry Pomeroy Castle.

He was saddened to see that the great project had not been completed, and so he went to the church to help out with the carvings on Sir Edward's tomb.

If you look closely you will see that the ruffs of the four daughters are finely executed by a mason whose hand once traced a remembered sketch onto a seat in Berry Castle. He had learnt it from one of his country's most famous artists who had predicted that mankind would not always be so earthbound.

Would he also have predicted that a ruin would become more famous than a completed building, and thus satisfy his ambition and peace of mind at last? If there are ghosts here then one of them must be that of Sir Edward, high up in the gatehouse, counting up the number of visitors who come under his portcullis year after year.

A Sonnet
to Berry Pomeroy Castle
Sue Hinds

A ruin sits buried in deep green Devon.
Arcs of light burn brilliantly at their height,
blue moments melting before the black night.
Silence is sounding, clouds close to heaven.
Stabbed woodland, golden shards uneven.
A draft of a Knight, a story takes fright.
Who was smothering shadows in the light,
that he stays here in this vale so uneven?
The daylight is melting, slipping away.
Florid shadows fading, the air turns evil.
Footsteps cover creeping death and decay.
it's a long way back to escape the devil.
The girls holding hands together, start to pray:
will we make it; we'll make it – yes we will?

Berry Pomeroy Castle
Pamela Sandry Gorman

Clouds incubate,
a thousand shadows
compose an eternity of
impressions.
Secret, moments
loom ghost-like.
Whisperings of murder.
Echoes bouncing off rocks –
fill the woods with mystery.
The river sinks lower
ashamed of the tragedy.
The castle falls into disrepair,
or should I say – DESPAIR?

The White Lady's Tale
Anna Lunk

EVEN NOW THE rumours persist, whispers up in the village, gossip down in the town. I can see no way to deny them, to wash my reputation clean. Yet if there's truth in these stories, it's only a small part of the whole. They say my sister haunts the castle, caught in the cruelty of incarceration. They have the wrong woman. My younger sister was too fond of colours to dress herself in this absence of colour. Her life was blameless. The innocent die well. If you should glimpse a pale shape passing down corridors, lingering at windows, it's me; the cruel elder sister, a woman tainted by remorse, seeking to explain, seeking redemption.

Yes, my sister was beautiful, very beautiful, her black hair sleek, strangely reflective, and her small delicate frame so very graceful. But she had a frailty and vulnerability about her which attracted the wrong sort of men. Those who weren't after the family name were looking for a woman to master; a boost to their own poor self image. And there were plenty of men who were after both riches and an obedient wife. Back then too many husbands viewed their wife as a possession with the same consideration that would be given to a piece of gold, or a precious jewel, something to reflect their own glory and to be kept tightly under lock and key. (Fortunately my own husband was quick to learn to give me certain liberties in exchange for my loyalty). So in some ways the life we chose for my sister was not that different to a married life.

But the truth was, my sister, for all her beauty, was not interested in men, at least not the men who were interested in her, sniffing round her skirts like dogs sniffing out their marks. Perhaps if the right man had come along... Well, who knows what might have been. Certainly I wouldn't have begrudged her a happy marriage. Even a good enough marriage can easily be tolerated when the husband is often away, as I knew well enough. All my consideration was for her care. Her frailty was not just a physical thing, but something in her mind. She was happy with her own company, with what she called her special occupations and she had an unusual capacity to be absorbed by the present moment, undisturbed by past memories or musings of what might unfold in the future. She was content enough sitting at a window looking down on the valley, her attention caught by the flight of birds, the glimpse of a deer between the trees. When she ventured beyond the castle walls it was never far, there was enough in the colours of the forest and the lush valley to last her a lifetime. Colour was the only companion she sought, her abiding interest.

It was true I envied her, but not her looks. No, it was her quiet contentment I envied, her ability to absent herself from others. She was never troubled by the hiring and firing of servants, the guest arrangements, the hunting parties. There were days when I longed to escape, as she so easily did, into small pleasures, away from the demands of castle life. Yes, I was jealous, but never of her beauty.

And afterwards, after that day when I found her down by the mill pond, then my only concern was to care for her, protect her. It was early autumn, the leaves just beginning to turn, the grasses by the track pale, not quite green, nor yet gold. She would have had a name for that particular shade, she had names for them all. I'm not sure how long she'd been gone from the castle, perhaps no more than an hour, perhaps longer. The men had gone out on their horses looking for wild boar; some had been sighted over towards Totnes. I had business with the miller, but had walked round the long way, wanting to catch a glimpse of sea from the hill. Just as my sister delighted in small details, in the veins on a leaf, the spring unfurling of a fern, I delighted in distances; the glimpse of a boat at sea, a rider coming over the brow of a hill, stories brought back by my husband and other soldiers of foreign lands. My thoughts were of the boat I'd seen, a trading vessel heading for land, too far out to identify. I imagined spices, fine cloths and a different kind of man. I must have walked right past her, my eyes on the track ahead, my mind on imaginary lovers. The business with the miller took time; matters of prices and what was owing and what was owed. He was a good miller, his flour fine and clean, but he was always keener to sell in town than supply his landlords with what was due.

Back then an alder grew by the side of the track, leaning towards the pond. She was propped against its trunk, her skirts bunched up around her waist, smears of blood down her thighs. I called out to her, but she didn't turn her head. I ran to her side, stroked her cheek, begged her to tell me what had happened, though I had idea enough. She stared out over the pond and its squabbling coots, a thin line of spittle at the corner of her mouth. She was breathing, but that was all the life there was in her. I stroked her hand, kissed her, begged her to talk to me, cupped her head in my hand, my face just inches from hers, wondered about slapping her cheeks, provoking her into life, but couldn't bring myself to do it. I couldn't leave her, but I couldn't lift her on my own. Dusk began to suck the colour away and the air grew cooler. I hoped the hunters would pass back this way. I hoped the miller would walk down to the pond. The rooks settled for the night and an uncommon quiet descended on the valley, no owls calling from the trees on the hillside, no rustlings of small mammals, not a breath of wind.

My husband found us. Worried by our absence on his return from the hunt he'd come looking for me, directed towards my business with the miller. He'd always been a good enough husband when he was at home, which wasn't often, but that night he showed a consideration and kindness I hadn't seen before. His full attention was on the task of getting my sister back up to the castle. Throwing his cloak around our shoulders he turned his horse back towards the castle to fetch men to help him. We soon had her back in her own bedroom where my maid had a fire ready and warm water to wash her. I would have sat with her all night, but my husband insisted I sleep in my own bed to rise the next day, rested and more able to assist in nursing my poor sister. It was hard to leave her, but the willing maid promised to fetch me should any crises occur, or should she awake from what seemed to be a sleep of kinds.

In the days that followed it seemed the whole castle was employed about her recovery. In the kitchen her favourite apple cakes were baked day after day, but it was all I could do to persuade her to take a few small bites, no more than a sparrow's peck. Wines were warmed and spiced with precious cloves and healing herbs, but the very act of drinking seemed to exhaust her. We had the musicians play soft airs under her window; she had always been fond of music, but she didn't seem to hear them. My husband forbade any loud noises and where there had previously been shouting voices, metallic clangings and the banging of doors, there was a sorrowful hush and all sound was muffled as if our lives were only half lived. But the weeks passed by and although my sister eventually left her bed, she never regained her speech. I suppose we should not have been surprised that violence committed on a frail personality should have tipped her into some kind of madness.

My husband did his best to find the culprit, turning his attention first on the guards, then the hunters and finally the local people. His questioning was ruthless, his sorrow transformed to anger, as it is with men. Eventually he was called away and I think we all knew the wretched man who had ruined my sister's life would never be found.

Life moved on, the years rolled by and my children were born, all six of them and they all thrived for which I was grateful. But my greatest care was always for my sister. With my growing family we had to move her to one of the lower rooms where she seemed a little happier. I think it was easier for her there, facing in towards the castle entrance, away from the valley and mill pond. Although she showed no desire to meet with anyone other than myself and her maid she liked to sit by the window watching people come and go. I like to think she eventually achieved a degree of her former happiness, busy at her colour work. We'd gather leaves, grasses, ferns for her and she'd spend hours making patterns with them, arranging them across the wooden boards. I never realised how many different greens there were until my sister's patterns became a part of my life. Even ferns come in many hues and the fresh bright ivy leaves of spring are nothing like the dark sombre over-wintered leaves. Spring always lifted her mood; such riches of new growth. We'd pick oak leaves from different trees so she could grade them across the floor from the early yellow tinged leaves to the more mature greener ones, and the beech leaves, they always brought a smile to her face. We'd bring branches into her room and she'd pluck leaves from them one by one, slowly and with some kind of design which I couldn't begin to guess at. When I visited her with her small supper I could barely find a patch of floor to stand on. Every evening there'd be a new pattern, sometimes a spiral of leaves leading to the centre of the room, the greens getting deeper as the spiral tightened. Sometimes I'd enter and think there was no pattern at all, just a random covering of leaves and grasses, but as my eyes became tuned to the detail I'd be able to see groupings of particular greens and textures, one group merging with the next in a most pleasing fashion.

Autumn and winter were always the worst times for my sister, for although we did the best to supply her with greenery there was less to choose from and less to delight her eye. She'd grow bored with her arranging and sit listless in her chair. I did my best to entertain her with small stories of my children's activities which I thought might amuse her. There was an unspoken understanding between us that her room was no place for growing minds, and besides she was too addicted to quiet to tolerate the conversation of children. Her appetite, always meagre, would decline dangerously close to starvation during these dark and damp winter days. I'd tempt her with her favourite delicacies, but it was hard work. Without her green leaves she had no appetite for life itself.

Then one winter we lost the battle to nourish her. My husband wanted me to force feed her, but I couldn't bring myself to do it. It was not what she wanted. How could I deny her escape from a life which she found so very hard to bare? But starve her? No, she starved herself.

It seemed that after her death some of her anxieties passed to me. I could no longer sleep easily, I was tormented by thoughts of what I might have done to save her, to bring her back to a normal life. I did my best, but it wasn't enough.

So, ghost hunter, reader of tales, when you see the white lady think of my anguish, a woman who meant well, tormented not only by the whispers and mutterings of blame, but her own inadequacies, a woman who was unable to save her own sister.

Do You See What I See?
Wendy Ruocco

Do you see what I see when you walk beneath its walls?
Does its magic make you think of lives long gone before?
And when you catch that fleeting glimpse of faces at a window high, do you
think your mind plays tricks? Do you walk on by?
With head bent low and not look back, convince yourself it's in the mind,
A trick of light and sky!
But I have seen them. I have seen them all...
Do you see what I see when you stop beneath the wall?

Do you feel what I feel when you stroll the empty rooms?
Do you feel the living near or feel the weight of doom?
Do you feel within its heart sad fragmented dreams, or do you feel that
nothing there is really as it seems?
Does it ever show its soul to those who ache to know,
Or do the spirits dwelling there favour those that turn and go?
I have felt it in my soul. I know it lives and breathes ...
Do you feel what I feel when unwilling you turn and leave?

Do you hear what I hear? Echoes from the past
In every stone that stands there still, in dungeons damp and dark.
Do you hear the mournful pleas to all who tread the stairs?
Don't flee! Please stay awhile with me, there's nothing here that scares!
When you hear their voices it's like lovers kiss, chill and brief it shivers skin
like early morning mist.
You think the day is turning chill, but hurry not away,
Berry Pomeroy speaks to you; she has so much to say,
Though you would scarcely know.
I am chosen. I have heard its voice come softly through in sighs...
Do you hear what I hear? Are you so surprised...?

Peril in Denim
Bob Mann

NOT SO MANY years ago, a group of us were sitting around a table near a log fire in an old-fashioned public bar: all browns and creams and dingy lights. It was a quiet, mid-week evening in January, and only a few predictable regulars were there, in pleasing contrast to the manic jollity of the previous month.

Old Smith and Carter were in their usual corner by the dart board, arguing about football in rich South Devon and East London accents, surrounded by a haze of cigar and pipesmoke (it was only, as I said, a few years ago, but it seems already a different world); and a couple of guys propped up the counter. Even the euchre going on next to us was subdued, and it is not a game normally played quietly. The student behind the bar, deeply engrossed in his book, was clearly not going to be disturbed too often.

I had a sudden sense of the long continuity of small town life as enshrined in the walls of these old inns and taverns, where for many generations, if not centuries, the doings of the community and its characters, as well as the wider world, have been endlessly discussed, analysed and commented upon. The Japanese philosopher and peace-builder Daisaku Ikeda, writing in praise of British democratic traditions, attributes them largely to our deep-rooted instinct for dialogue and debate, no doubt an inevitable result of our rich ethnic, linguistic and cultural mix. It is 'practised,' he says, 'in the parliament' (one *could* be cynical about that), but its origin is 'in the pubs.'

I let my imagination range for a while through time, trying to grasp exactly what it would have been like to experience what we call 'history,' but was once the reality of the present moment. How did those drinking here react to the news of Trafalgar, when it was first brought to them? There were nineteen Totnesians at the battle, in various roles on various ships, three of them only in their teens (though no one at the time, of course, would have had that information). How many of them ever came home, and maybe warmed themselves at this fireplace, while they gazed into their pewter mugs and tried to drown the memories of blood and screaming? What were they talking about at the bar as Scott reached the South Pole, or when Hitler moved into Czechoslovakia? Pointless, impossible questions, I know, but part of me is always asking them.

I was brought back to an awareness of the present when somebody at the table invoked the name of Berry Pomeroy Castle, and immediately my mind was at that archetypal Romantic ruin a couple of miles or so across the fields and woods, reputed to be the most haunted in England.

Mention the place, and you know you'll be telling ghost stories for the next half hour. We all duly did so, sharing tales of apparitions, camera and engine failure, strange smells and sounds, feelings of going back in time, and the powerful sense of unreasonable fear that will suddenly descend on visitors who have been wandering happily around the shattered halls. I said that I have experienced this a few times, but that the fear is never for myself; it only happens if I'm there with a female friend or loved one, and I'm suddenly convinced that if I don't get her away immediately, something awful is going to happen to her. Usually she feels nothing untoward, and is extremely annoyed at my insistence that we go.

Mike related the tale, told to him by a friend of the person it happened to (or something like that), in which someone drove out there to brood over an argument he'd had with his girlfriend. (Why would anyone in their right mind go to Berry Pomeroy Castle in such an emotional state?). He'd suddenly felt that some entity had got into the car with him. He was so terrified that he drove straight to his parents' place in Yorkshire. Whatever it was stayed with him until the early hours, when it vanished on the North York Moors, no doubt returning instantly to the castle (if it hadn't been simultaneously there all along).

I threw in the knowledge that Robert Graves had been living nearby while he was writing *The White Goddess*, that strange study of the Muse, and that he mentions ghostly ladies as one of her commoner manifestations; he had, himself, been driven away from the castle by a sense of appalling evil in its very stones.

Jeff offered a story about some people he knew, who went there one night, and heard music in the woods. Walking towards the castle, they came upon a group of musicians, dressed in authentic late Elizabethan or early Jacobean costume. One of his friends even recognised the piece they were playing (*Fantasia*, by William Mundy, I think). They assumed at first that it was an Early Music group rehearsing, but why so late at night, in the woods, and in full costume? Then, suddenly, the light changed, and the musicians and music disappeared, and they were all alone in the dark forest.

I went for another drink. The two old boys in the corner had now got onto horse racing. I asked the guy behind the bar what he was reading.

'*The Way to Attain*, by a 17th century French writer called Beroalde de Verville. Sort of Rabelaisian, but cruder.'

'Ah yes, the canon of Tours. He's the one who has the story of the farting prostitute, isn't he,' I replied.

'That's him!'

'The way to attain what, though?'

'I haven't worked that out, yet.'

Back at the table I heard Nick say 'Well, I don't know about ghosts, but I've been haunted since I went there in the summer. I fell in love twice in one day.'

We all sighed gently, because Nick was a highly susceptible soul who would fall in love with every pretty girl who gave him even the slightest attention. A barmaid only had to smile as she handed him his change, and he was smitten. He would agonise for hours over a young woman's tone of voice when saying 'Hullo,' and whether it meant he had a chance with her. He was twenty-eight at the time, and not unattractive to women, but his schoolboy vulnerability and neediness sent most of them away.

'Tell us,' said Jeff.

'Well, I go there a lot in the summer on my days off, and I was wandering around one afternoon when I saw this unbelievably beautiful blonde girl. She was a bit like the one I fancy in the Kingsbridge, you know?'

We did.

'But there was something about her I'd never experienced before. She was wearing a thin white cotton shirt and pants [Nick's descriptions of form, costume and adornment were always lovingly detailed], and the shape of her was... oh, well, all I can say is that I've dreamed of her since. She was on the bit that leads to the tower with the dungeon, and she gave me such a smile as I passed that I nearly melted. But she must have left soon after, because I didn't see her again.'

He trailed off, his eyes on some distant scene.

'You said you fell in love twice,' prompted Mike.

'Yes, well, about ten minutes later I walked into that room where the fireplace is, and there was a gorgeous dark-haired girl in jeans and a denim jacket standing in there. She was a bit older and more voluptuous than the first. She was lovely, but she didn't look very happy, and I longed to hug and comfort her. She gave me a sad smile, and went out to where the cliff falls away, and when I followed I was so distracted by the sight of her from behind that I nearly slipped. Then she was gone. I'd love to see either of them again. I've been back several times, but they're never around.'

I looked him straight in the eye, and spoke as dramatically as I could.

'On no account should you go looking for either of those young women again. Indeed, I strongly advise you never to go back to Berry Pomeroy Castle, at least not on your own. Those girls were not of this world, and you were in great peril. You could have fallen out of time, and wandered, eternally, in a limbo of shadows and despair.' (I had recently discovered the work of the Californian fantasist Clark Ashton Smith, and was consciously modelling my speech on his prose poem 'The Peril that Lurks Among Ruins.' Seek it out...).

'What on earth do you mean?' asked Jeff.

'Just let me get another pint, and I'll tell you.'

They watched me in stunned silence as I went to the bar. A log shifted its position in the fire, and the sparks flew up. Old Carter and Smith were now discussing the differences between British and American publishers. Though they both play on being good old working class boys, it is thirty years since they did anything more manual than carrying their manuscripts to the Post Office (though I suppose, now, they use email, like everyone else). They are novelists: hard-boiled thrillers and talking animal sagas respectively.

I got my pint and sat down.

'Do you know what is meant by Cultural Tracking?' I asked. Nobody did.

'It's a term used by researchers into the paranormal to describe the ways in which strange phenomena manifest according to the beliefs and expectations of the witnesses. People see what they want to see, or are told they will see. In the pre-industrial countryside you had pixies and fairy folk who turned the milk sour and got you lost on the moors. Now you're abducted by little grey entities with big eyes, who do nasty experiments on you. Encountering either plays havoc with the sense of passing time.

'UFOs are always just a little in advance of human technology, but not so much as to be incomprehensible. So in the 1890s and 1900s, when a lot of energy was going into the creation of flying machines, strange forms in the sky were like airships, and the usual explanation was quite reasonable: some millionaire was test-flying his new invention, which would soon be unveiled to the world. But, somehow, it never was. During the 1930s, huge boat-planes were seen in the skies and lakes of northern Europe. People guessed they must be German, but when the war came, it was obvious that Germany had no such craft, and nor did anyone else. When the space age began, we started getting flying saucers full of fair-haired aliens who claimed to be from Venus or Mars. Now we know both to be uninhabitable, they're from another dimension. Same archetypes: small, slightly dangerous beings, weird machines in the sky, but always fitting in with the socio-cultural beliefs, fears and anxieties of the times.'

I took a long pull at my pint.

'Now, what are the most famous traditional ghosts at Berry Pomeroy Castle? The White Lady, who was supposedly starved to death in a dungeon by her jealous sister, and who walks along the ramparts beckoning to you to join her in the depths below (a perfect illustration, by the way, of the Jungian Anima, and the dangers of repressing her), and the Blue Lady, who had a child by her own father and smothered it, and who now walks in eternal anguish through the castle, and lures unsuspecting men to dangerous parts of the ruins.'

I looked straight at Nick. 'You have seen them both, and you had a very fortunate escape.'

He stared back in amazement. 'But those weren't ghosts, for godsake! They were flesh and blood girls. They were from today, not centuries ago!'

'They were the White and Blue Ladies of Berry Pomeroy Castle,' I insisted. 'They've been around a long time. You don't think they're going to appear as semi-transparent figures in long, flowing medieval dresses and Pre-Raphaelite hairstyles? That wouldn't fool anyone. Any guy would just say, "Shit, there's the White and Blue Ladies, better get the hell out of here!" No, they're going to be wearing sexy tight cotton trousers and shirts, and blue denim, and look like the girls you see in the street and fancy a hundred times a day. Stay away from those ruins, lest you fall from the world, and remain forever a lost shadow among shadows!'

At that moment the barman gently announced last orders, and we all concentrated on refilling our glasses, and the evening wound down with talk of a less consequential nature.

§

I now see, anyway, that I was wrong, at least in part. Not about Nick seeing the ghostly ladies, because that is undoubtedly who they were, but about their meaning for him.

I don't know if he ever did go back to the castle in search of those visions of beautiful young womanhood. But sharing with us his encounter with them certainly worked a deep magic in his life. Soon afterwards, he began to realise, or finally acknowledge, that his great love and reverence for the feminine was not so much a yearning to possess, as a yearning to become; and he embarked on a brave and determined journey towards fulfilment as Nicole.

So maybe we malign and fear those ladies a little too much. Maybe, next time we're at the castle, instead of fleeing in terror the moment they appear, we should seek them out, and follow where they lead, as Nick was prepared to do, and listen, with our lives, to whatever message they might have for us.

The White Roses
of Berry Pomeroy
Susan Taylor

Five centuries ago, this place appeared invincible;
its gun emplacements the most advanced in the kingdom,
because it was an outpost built on fear.
The Pomeroy family wore white roses,
were white roses, marooned on an escarpment
watching over green hills and hams
where all the gardens, noble to humble
festered with roses as red as freshly opened wounds.

The habits of Devon were cut-throat then,
neighbour hacked neighbour for profit,
but Berry's new castle was aptly forbidding.
The eldest son departed with troops to Tewkesbury
to prove the white gleam of his weapons
was lethal, among the gathering red.
First in line, battle ready, he was triumphant,
and dead from the fight in a few short days.

When the Pomeroys weakened, the Seymours bought
into Berry with rank and display of fortune.
They rocked the next century with flamboyance,
built a luxurious wing, which rose around
window bays, flying up into the path of the light.
The eerie stacks that supported these structures
are lamentable now, ragged as columns
of wax, where glittering lifestyles burned away.

We see, by the matchwood model in the Gatehouse,
how gleaming those wings were, how terrifyingly rich
their display and we hear how their ladies stood
behind fabulous arbours of glass to watch
the slaughter of cattle on the terrace below them,
how Colonel Edward, second baronet,
named one of his warships 'Samaritan' and sent it
to pillage French fishing boats in the English Channel.

Small wonder this flower of a place ran to seed
and was left ravaged and strange, stripped
of its pretty interior: marble carvings, pillars,
bright tapestries carted towards the capital.
We stare up through the spaces left by glass,
sense how ghosts have entrenched themselves here:
blue lady of sky, white lady of cloud clinging to ruin,
long out of reach of the thorns on the carmine roses.

A Short Tale of Berry Pomeroy
Wendy Ruocco

THE PRETTY YOUNG woman settled herself in the castle grounds, in the open area that would once have been the castle bailey. She wriggled herself comfortably into the cold surface of a piece of fallen masonry, and peeled open her sketchpad. Today she would draw. At least, that's what her thoughts determined: put something onto paper.

Today she would try to ignore the castle's magnetism, not let its stillness enter her head and lull her into dreaming of its past.

She loved the castle. It was as familiar to her as the hand that now put pencil to paper. Seeking inspiration, she looked with an artist's eye for a quirky angle, an out of the ordinary viewpoint. She sketched a few half-hearted outlines, smudging the dusty charcoal into vague shapes with her finger.

Brittle May sunshine, shot through with cloud, threw shadows on the grass, indigo and viridian; the dark patches formed, melted, then formed again, gliding across the green swathe as if they were guardians of the past.

Seemingly void of any other visitors, peaceful, the castle breathed an ancient rhythmic pulse that tingled every nerve ending in her body. It wrapped her in a familiar embrace.

The castle and its unique surroundings held no fear for her. That's why she found herself here so often. Far from feeling uneasy, overlooked by windows in high floorless walls, she believed that the ghosts and spirits who dwelt here were friendly ones, that they welcomed her.

Above the roofless chapel, where ferns grew from between damp stones, some crows argued, cawing raucously. Shielding her eyes she watched their antics as they rose flapping into the air, before dropping back onto the stone ramparts. Making strange guttural sounds in their throats, they preened glossy black feathers as if uninterested, before again hopping into the fray.

But enough bird watching! She had come to draw, make a picture. She bent her head, blinking from the light, and tried to concentrate. Just some rough sketches; was it really so difficult? Then, as she put charcoal to paper, the hammering of woodpeckers caused her attention to wander once more. Mother Nature, and her ploys to keep her from her task? She smiled at her silliness.

Beyond the castle tall larches swayed in the woods, keeping time with the drumming birds, and the wind soughed in the tree tops like music, or the whispering of many voices. The sounds lulled her. For a fleeting moment, less than a heartbeat, she had the eeriest sensation of being watched; through half closed eyes she studied the curtain wall until drowsiness claimed her. Once she succumbed to the bliss of sleep, her subconscious took over; willing that which her wakeful mind would not....

With a jolt she awoke, cold and momentarily confused as to where she was. Someone, something, had pulled at her hair – no imaginary sensation, but a real tug, though gentle, like a small child's dare. She glanced irritably behind and quickly back again, not knowing quite what she might see; a tease laughing at her discomfort?

It was then she saw him, dressed unmistakeably in knightly garb, just inside the gatehouse, veiled by violet shadow, but lit from behind by a single shaft of sunlight. In the darkness of the passageway it fragmented about his person like shards of broken glass.

He stepped from the shadow and the light stayed with him, not harsh now but soft like a halo, emanating from, rather than illuminating, his form. Though his eyes were in shadow, she felt their intensity blistering her senses as he watched; even without seeing, she knew them to be sea green, with sparks of emerald and cobalt...

The sketch pad slid to the ground with less rustle than an oak leaf shaken by autumn's breeze. She glanced down quickly when it caught the hem of her gown, almost afraid to look away for fear the vision before her might disappear. Why, she wondered, did bare toes peep from beneath azure velvet, for surely she had worn jeans today!

He stretched his arm towards her and beckoned, just a curling of the fingers, the slightest movement of his hand; 'come!' – the gesture was clear. This was no command, more a silent plea.

Like a moth fluttering gaily towards the radiance of death, she went eagerly to him...

On awakening, she had the distinct sensation of having been set free, as if no longer earthly-bound. She'd observed herself from outside, head bent intently over the paper; strangely there had been no desire to re-enter or take possession of her body.

The crows still squabbled, but their cries were distant. A family had stopped to look at her. How strangely they stooped to peer and frown. Why? She feared they may even reach out and touch her.

Her feet were chilled, the skin white against the grass, and her toes looked rather odd, with bright pink varnish, and she had no recollection of removing her trainers. Maybe that's why people were curious. 'Another weird artist type,' they probably muttered. She saw their lips moving but heard no sound. She rose. How light, and high above the ground, her body felt. The watchers melted back, allowed her to pass; two children, wide-eyed, turned their little faces into a woman's hip.

The path that had brought her to the castle now seemed never ending. Her feet hurt and she stopped; how careless to leave behind her trainers! Quite bizarre! She thought, 'I must go back'. She turned; azure velvet twisted around her ankles, threatened to trip her.

At the bottom of the pathway she saw him. A smile played clearly across his lips, though his eyes were hidden.

With outstretched arm he beckoned. No grand gesture, just a slight impatience to the curling fingers. 'Come,' they invited...

She went to him.

The sketchbook lay where it had fallen, beside a block of lichen-covered masonry. Dew-sodden, the empty pages flapped damply in the sudden afternoon chill.

St Margaret's Tower, Berry Pomeroy Castle
Simon Williams

Black blown white, the nights enshroud her,
down the spiral stair, in that tight place
like soot, the verdigris of gunpowder.

They say a trick of birth endowed her
with beauty not found in her sister's face.
Black blown white, the nights enshroud her

in the dungeon, where years before the louder
cry of cannon left its own sour trace;
soot, the verdigris of gunpowder.

Without a battened door, you wonder how the
room can be a prison, a holding place,
where, black blown white, the nights enshroud her.

Would she take a little broth or chowder
with the fat of candles smoking up this vaulted face,
laying soot, the verdigris of gunpowder?

Though her sister never once allowed her
to exercise along the rampart terrace,
now, black blown white, the nights enshroud her
like soot, the verdigris of gunpowder.

Berry Pomeroy – The Thoughts of a Witch

Debbie Miller-Wright

THE LONG LANE of autumn laid the way to the place I can no longer enter.

Late summer was vanishing. Smells of earthly movements and undiscovered secrets in the ground on either side of the entranceway; sun slowly moving round, giving a soft sheen of positive onto the leaves and shiny bark of the birch.

A pleasant memory, full of scent and emotion, of being close to nature, as I so love to be.

So many stories of this place have been told by so many, each with its unfounded little twist of horror to tease the human senses and curiosity, and encourage adventure!

I went forwards to the boundary of the property with trepidation. There was an un-rest within me. I do listen to tales of the supernatural as a rule, I always have done, due to what I have seen and experienced in the past. I also think that being a Witch makes you a little more open to superstitions and tales than others.

The feeling though, was more of a voice, a voice clearly saying to me,

'Do not walk forth, do not enter; this is for your own sanity, you must not enter.'

This feeling was slightly worrying, (my first understatement), but I was willing to work through it, to argue against it, throw on my 'naïve hat' and walk on in.

The Gatehouse. My most used words, when asked about Berry Pomeroy Castle, as I can no longer walk through this new entranceway. I have no idea as to whether it is a new entranceway or not, but I get a feeling that it is built to cover up some ghastly deed. I have no idea what, though, as yet.

First signs for me of things beyond my control are Goosebumps. I first get them under my jaw, along the bone line. A slight emotional breeze to the jaw reacts with my skin's pores, making them rise in a suspicious defence. They spread, ever worried for my fate, down my neck and along the underside of each arm to finish superbly on my forearm giving a positive identification of fear!

On entering the Gatehouse the bumps went on a mission of epic proportions, spreading all over my body, eventually to my skull.

This was my first experience of why a person's hair 'stands on end' due to fear. The head bumps! A sure sign to me now.

The bumps of fear remained ever present, moving over my body like a crowd-wave at a football match, constantly on the move, keeping my wits exactly where they should be, right on edge where I needed them. I've never likened my wits to an emergency service before this day, but I will forever, now.

As I made my way through, further into the grounds, I became aware of a pressure on the base of my neck, at the rear, as though someone had a hand resting there, guiding my movement.

I have only experienced this feeling once since then, at Hexworthy on Dartmoor. What a very wrong place that is!

The pressure on my neck grew stronger and I had the feeling that someone was moving closer and closer to me. I half expected someone to whisper in my ear. I almost felt their breath withdraw as they inhaled to speak.

I had a sudden need for comfort. I wanted a small hiding place to curl up in, closed away from the fear.

I moved forwards into the ruins to find such a place of comfort. No one else was around.

Everyone had gone back to their lives, away from this beautiful county. I was alone.

My one and only comfort was the countryside around me, but the woodland beneath held such sinister thoughts that it distracted slightly from this beauty. This I can confirm is my second, and last, understatement.

The dips and hills in South Devon are some of the most beautiful and inspiring I have seen and I thank Mother Nature for putting some beauty around this otherwise negative and evil spot.

I ambled beneath the high walls of what was once a beautiful house, but the feelings for me were of attitude, wealth, a feeling of superiority without grounding and a need to be seen as grand, but without the moral substance to back it up.

I felt death, departure and lack of forgiveness. I felt torture and triumph, all in the same ill-meaning tormentor. I walked further round, trying to ignore the ever-fluctuating bumps of fear. There was also a feeling of slight nausea and anxiety and to accompany that, anger.

A quick mental check, to ascertain at what point my hormone levels were in the month, confirmed that I should have been in fact as 'Happy as Larry!'

I was growing more anxious and grumpy and not requiring to see anymore. Maybe I was coming down with something. Time to get back? I moved slowly from the far corner, overlooking the woodland and the area of the well.

As I passed the high walls and relics of what was once a beautiful extravagant home I experienced feelings of sadness. The Castle at Berry Pomeroy is a place of hard work with no gratitude, a place of constant sadness and a longing to be elsewhere.

I know I certainly wanted to be elsewhere, so I left the ruins behind.

I am sure that stories affect the reality of thought, but I also know what I personally felt that day.

I saw no visions, no ghosts, no White Lady, nothing bad happened to me when I left, but I will never forget those feelings of evil and uncertainty, of despair and sadness.

If I were ever to return, it would be with company, and only just to see if I wasn't completely unjustified in my feelings that day.

See for yourself?

Pomeroy's Leap
Catherine Smith

The brothers looked out 'cross the hills
and knew their time was near.
This wicked siege had been in place
for nigh on one whole year.

The castle was surrounded now
with men on every side.
The Pomeroys had no escape,
but they still had their pride.

They knew that they could not defeat
the might of this young king,
yet from his Book of Common Prayer
their voices would not sing.

With one accord they left the room
summoning their pages.
The glory of their deaths they knew
would echo down the ages.

The only way to save their name
was to die with honour
and so they called out clear and true
to be brought their armour.

The tears fell from their pages' eyes
as they dressed the brothers,
knowing they went to their deaths
for the sake of others.

As they were clad from head to toe
in finest battledress
they sent their blessings to their kin
and made their last requests.

And yet the thing that made a knight
was not that which he wore;
it was the steed on which he rode
at all times safe and sure.

To the ramparts, to the brothers
the horses were brought forth.
A blindfold placed across their eyes,
their noses turned due north.

Upon their backs the brothers jumped
and bellowed to the King:
'We die for Devon and for freedom
and the glory it will bring.'

The hooves rang out 'cross the stonework,
the horses then took flight.
The brothers leapt out to their freedom
and to defend their rights.

The men around the precipice
called out in shock and awe.
The brothers and, it must be said,
their horses, were no more.

They'd made their stand, they'd named their terms
and so they died with joy,
knowing that they had brought honour
to the name of Pomeroy.

The White Lady
Pamela Sandry Gorman

Ghostly whisperings of death,
of magic and of lost love.
A thousand shadows lingered
as her life's blood slowly
seeped into surrounding rocks.
The moon loomed
over the castle turrets.
The imprisoned sister's
rotting white robes
clung to her wasted shape.
Plaintive songs can
sometimes be heard
deep into the night –
an eternity of waiting.
Revenge will be sweet.
Till then her soul hovers,
lingers, merges, mingles,
watching and praying
for the time to come.

The Story of a Vision
and a Disappearance
Bob Mann

'What beck'ning ghost, along the moonlight shade
Invites my steps, and points to yonder glade?'

Pope, 'Elegy to the Memory of an Unfortunate Lady'

LAST AUTUMN [2009], AS you may remember, English Heritage felt the need to cut down the old beech tree in front of Berry Pomeroy Castle, the one that had long been known as the Wishing Tree. It was right next to the steep pathway leading down to the Gatcombe valley. In fact, much of the trunk is still there; they only removed the upper part and the branches. But what they cut down produced a lot of wood, and a friend who once worked at the castle offered to get me a piece. I accepted.

Soon afterwards I wrote a very short tale which some of my friends received instead of a Christmas card. In it, I described how I carried the piece of wood home, put it down on the lawn and walked around it, backwards, three times, simultaneously expressing my desires to the universe. I then found myself falling hundreds of feet from a precipitous cliff. It was a very tongue-in-cheek little story, which I threw off quickly, based on the point that the tree was in quite a dangerous place to walk around anyway, let alone backwards. What was depressing was that so few readers got it.

I now wish I hadn't written it at all.

I still have my lump of the tree, though it is next to the fence, and cannot be walked around. I glance at it occasionally through the window, but obliquely, and not for long. I have decided that, as with the sun, it is best not to gaze at it too directly.

Mark and David also had pieces of the tree, and, as far as I know, they remain well and happy. The friend who acquired them for us, and has one herself, is still safe. But Steve, who got a lump of it as well, seems not to have been so fortunate, although I doubt whether anyone, until now, ever thought of associating his disappearance, last February, with his possession of a piece of old wood. It may be a completely mad idea. But, having studied and pondered upon the account you are about to read, I have a strong feeling that there is a connection.

None of us knew him that well. There is an informal group of us who go for a walk on Dartmoor once a month, followed by a meal in a nearby village pub. He came along a few times, and would also occasionally meet up with some of us in the Bay Horse. He shared our interest in folklore and the paranormal, but I talked to him mainly about the supernatural in literature, which the others know less about and find less absorbing (because, they reckon, it's all 'made up,' and therefore not 'real'). He had a good knowledge of the works of classic horror and supernatural writers like M. R. James, Arthur Machen, Mark Samuels, Quentin S. Crisp, Algernon Blackwood and the rest, and had written a few tales of his own, in clever imitation of some of their different styles.

Looking back, I realise how he would have loved to have been there in May, when I went, with four other enthusiasts – including the two writers in the above list who didn't die decades ago – on that strange expedition to Broadhempston and Woodland churchyards, in the beautiful countryside between Totnes and Newton Abbot, in search of H. P. Lovecraft's South Devon roots. I may, eventually, find the courage to describe that weekend, and the dreadful revelations to which it inexorably led – doing so would certainly refute the idea that fictional horrors are in any way 'unreal!' (Work that one out). One of the worst aspects of the whole experience for me, as a local loyalist, was the contrast between the environment we were in, so lovely, familiar and apparently so *safe*, and the barely nameable terrors we unwittingly unleashed...

On second thoughts, perhaps it is good that Steve was spared the traumas we all suffered, and continue to suffer.

Anyway. When he just vanished from his home one day in February, leaving not a trace, Steve was apparently in good health. He seemed happy in his relationship with his partner, Sue, and in his work at the South Hams District Council Planning Department. He had no financial problems and did not, as far as anyone knew, suffer from depression. Thousands of people disappear in this country every year, of course, and unless the police have reason to believe a crime has been committed, there is very little that can be done about it. Sue and his ageing parents have gradually begun to rebuild their lives, although closure, at least for the old couple, has not come.

A week or so ago, Sue, whom I have quietly loved since I first saw her, contacted me to say that she had found a story on his computer, which he seems to have been writing just before his disappearance. She thought I might find it of interest. I asked her to email it to me, and, when it arrived I made myself a coffee and sat down to read it. At first it seemed like a pleasing pastiche of M. R. James. Now... well, let me give you the gist of the tale, and you can decide for yourselves.

After briefly saying how he came to have the piece of beechwood, Steve describes how he, too, placed it in his garden, in front of the hedge, where it was visible from his kitchen window. Like my piece, it was not from the main trunk, but from a branch. Three smaller branches had originally grown from it, but these had been cut off and were now mere protuberances. One dark winter afternoon, shortly after returning from work, and still waiting for Sue to get home, he found himself looking out at it in the gloom.

> As I gazed at it, it seemed to shimmer, and I had a strange impression of the texture being more like stone than wood; a knothole was like a vacant, glass-less window. I seemed to leave my body and be carried down an endless corridor, as huge vistas of time opened up around me. Then suddenly I was back in my kitchen, dizzy and shaken. I quickly pulled the blind down on the window, and turned on the light.

A few days later, at the same time of day, and again alone in the house, he found himself once more absorbed in looking out at his log.

> Again I had the illusion it was stone rather than wood. It looked somehow squarer than it had been; the two protuberances on the left appeared straighter and the one on the right was also different. I forced myself to look away.

The following day, he could no longer refuse to see what was happening.

The protuberances on the left were now, unmistakeably, two towers of a gatehouse; the main bulk of the log was a ruined mansion inside a surrounding wall; the other protuberance was St Margaret's Tower. It was a perfect scale model of the castle. I gazed at it, in amazement, and terror. 'This is just a projection,' I thought. 'Ink blots. Tea leaves. Trees on a hillside. It's just association: I'm putting the shape of the castle there. It hasn't really changed its form. It's just my mind doing it. My unconscious mind knows where the log came from, and that I'm interested in the castle and its legends. I can stop, and see it as it really is, a lump of old wood.' I shut my eyes, and said 'right, now I'm going to look again and it will be a log.' I opened my eyes, and it was a perfect scale model of Berry Pomeroy Castle. I rushed into the back garden and went to the log. It was a lump of beechwood with some smaller lumps on it, where once branches had been. I thought of flinging it away as far as I could, or giving it to my neighbour to burn, but something stopped me. 'What is there to be afraid of?' I thought. 'This is actually really interesting. I'm not mad. I can handle daily life as well as I ever could. Why not just go with it, and see what happens?'

The next afternoon, he made himself look out as soon as he got home, and the log had already assumed the shape of the castle.

Before long, I was no longer looking through a window at a scale model of Berry Pomeroy Castle. I was out there, standing in front of the castle itself, which loomed over me in the moonlight. And then I saw it — a movement to the right, and there was a white figure, gliding along the Ramparts from the direction of St Margaret's Tower. The White Lady! The ghost of the lovely girl who was imprisoned in the tower by her sister, and who lures men to their doom by beckoning to them, inviting them to join her in the depths! With a huge effort I said 'No! I will NOT LET THIS HAPPEN!' and forced myself to be back in my kitchen. I pulled down the blind with such violence that it nearly came away completely. Just then Sue came in, and looked at me with a startled expression. 'What's the matter? You look like you've seen a ghost,' she said. 'It's all right, just a stressful day,' I replied, and kissed her. 'I'm getting rid of that thing tomorrow,' I decided.

There the tale ends. I read it several times, thinking it was quite effective, though maybe rather too obviously based on James's *The Mezzotint*. With a bit of editing, it would be worth putting into the collection of stories and poems, inspired by the castle, that the Longmarsh Press planned to publish the following year. A nice tribute to Steve's memory, I thought.

But over the next few days, I found myself strangely troubled by the story, and increasingly reluctant to look out at my own log. Then Sue rang me, and asked what I thought of Steve's tale. I said what I have said here, but she somehow knew how I was feeling. 'I know it sounds mad,' she said, 'but do you think there could just be some truth in it? Do you think maybe he did...'

'Go back the next night, and accept the White Lady's invitation?' I finished for her.

'It's impossible, I know. But...yes.'

I sighed. 'I don't know. That place can have a strange influence on some people, as I'm well aware. Do you still have the log, by the way? I'd like to have a look at it.'

'No. It disappeared the same time as he did. I've no idea what happened to it.'

§

I have walked in the vicinity of the castle a few times since that conversation, in the woods and down into the valley by the ponds. I have deliberately not looked around for a lump of the Wishing Tree with three protuberances on it, nor will I in the future. But I suspect that it is there, somewhere. Maybe I'll end up taking mine back, one day, as well. I don't want to, but I have a feeling my wishes don't really come into it.

§

I finished the story, read through it, made a few changes, then closed the computer and went eagerly to bed. Sue enfolded me deliciously with her nakedness. She looked imploringly at me. 'He won't ever be found, will he?' she said.

'No, of course not. It's impossible.' An image of the ponds below the castle slipped into my mind, but I ignored it.

'What are we going to do? I hate all this waiting.'

'We'll start meeting for a drink occasionally, and let people get used to seeing us around, then, after about six months, we'll tell everyone we're moving in together.'

Follow Me Down
Peter Cowlam

I guess at how these addictions turned
Into today's stone mortuary, a cold world
Of daylight where everything is neglect –
My suburbia a reference point
Where the fences pale, and the way is bindweed
Heaped on a path running dawn to dawn.

I recall, by whatever stimulant,
Yellow lamplight on the unearthly presence
Of bottled ink, made a phantasmic
Diamond brightness, and how in a garble
Of half-chewed sentences I announced
All transformations were possible.

That mesmerising flicker shared its music
In the first dead hours when the city
Shut its eyes. Seductive chords, and a depth
Of basses voiced natural opposition
To the world of deserted streets, in a shade
Of sleepy blue in every blanked-out house.

I vied for instant sachets, the currency
Notes or IOUs, set in the same clutter
Of discarded poker hands, while magic
Particles, poured onto a vanity glass,
Assumed meticulous regimentation
Under a guiding hand with a razor blade.

I remember the disintegration
These hallucinations meted out,

Off-colour chords decaying into discord,
Pleasure contra dependency, the insane
Daily pursuit of the paradise
Prophets and poets had shrilled about.

Once, under the hard dead light of dawn,
I found myself in a neighbourhood
More angular than my own, and there pleaded
With a boy laden with newspapers,
Not entirely confident I'd understood
His directions home, and stumbled away.

Materiality threatened its return
In the brittle textures of twilight,
When I had spent hours after midnight
Afloat with the garbage piled in a hotel
Yard, lost to a soft delusional light
And a weightless elevation.

Now somehow I'm here,
In the ruins of Berry Pomeroy Castle,
In a cascade from old nightmares to new,
In a white ache, under a blue light,
Where a disembodied voice is urging me
On, with a 'Follow me down'—

And I tell myself I don't know how this happened.

The Way Back
Idris W. Izzard

LEGENDS TELL OF many ghosts at Berry Pomeroy Castle, and enthusiasts of the paranormal say it houses several different kinds. However, some of the most famous aren't really ghosts at all, not spirits anyway, just some sort of recording – events imprinted on the fabric of spacetime. These so-called residual energy hauntings replay periodically, or when someone living somehow triggers a playback.

The real, living ghosts are the more dangerous type, but sometimes they don't know they're dead. Lost souls wander piteously, seeking comfort in a world they no longer understand and where they no longer have any place. Some mediums seek them out to lead them into the light of spiritual realisation. But not many.

There is a well-known haunting at Berry Pomeroy Castle, in which a terrified young woman is fleeing up stairs. She has been seen repeatedly, in exactly the same manner, just like a recording with her raw emotion seemingly fixed in the very stone of the structure. But she could be more than just an inert impression – she could be a conscious soul caught in a cruel web. In her fatal panic she may be oblivious to years, even centuries grinding past.

She may be fully alive in every meaningful sense, just endlessly repeating her final moments, desperate for something to change but finding no way out. We've all had nights of tossing and turning, wrestling with a problem. We churn our thoughts, memories and imagination, until the annihilation of exhaustion or the grey light of dawn puts an end to our anguish. Her whole being may be so intent on escaping the death that pursues her that she has been enduring the agony of false hope.

Any psychic, sensitive, and medium would love to save such a suffering soul, but how many would dare approach her, let alone interrupt the headlong flight of such a fierce turn of mind? To reach out into the realm of the dead, to clutch the spirit of living nightmare, grip it tighter than the bonds of death itself, and tear the phantom from its frenzied course... To confront centuried madness, and talk it down.

I may hope her presence is just an insentient stain on the reputation of the castle, a scar of dishonour on a grim page in its history. That, and nothing more. But even if she is alive in death, I feel there may be a chance for her liberation. There may indeed.

One day, science could reveal all, and exorcise the entire spectrum of mankind's seemingly eternal hopes and fears about the afterlife. Perhaps it already has, and until recently I would have agreed with the sceptic that while ghosts make good stories, there is no real truth in them. But now, I wonder. In the quiet reaches of the night I find myself almost hoping some spiritual truth may yet be found in the mystery of life's many dimensions – a truth to set us finally free.

I am too conventional to relish such an unimaginable adventure, but I have witnessed a dear friend set out on just such a voyage. I was alone with him at the hospital after the accident, and it was his dying wish for his spirit to depart for its spiritual home. Who can say such wishes may not sometimes be granted?

His pain was controllable but he wasn't expected to live more than an hour. I sat with him, conversing in intense snatches as he drifted in and out of consciousness.

'I only went there once,' he moaned. 'I always meant to return. I kept putting it off. Never put things off! I always knew it would be there tomorrow. And it will be, but I shan't, eh?'

I hadn't a clue what he was thinking of, and muttered something optimistic about his recovery.

'No,' he said. 'I can barely keep inside my body. It's broken, and I can't stay. It's my time – earlier than I thought – but it's close. Don't try to hold me, it'll hurt both of us. Better I leave in peace.'

I promised him I would not make a fuss, and for a few minutes he was calm and breathed deeply as if asleep. When he reopened his eyes he fixed on me with eyes clear and bright, untainted by that fatal lethargy which would have seen him slip quietly away.

He was suddenly possessed of tremendous vitality. I had seen that change in him happen many times. I couldn't take my eyes from him – his momentary bewilderment as an idea swept through his mind was a powerful part of his charisma – and the next instant he could be as alert as a wild creature poised to pounce.

'I wonder,' he whispered.

What?

'I may go there yet.'

Where?

'Down the leafy lane of years gone by, all the way to that enchanted place bathed in the warm, bright sunshine of youth where in a few brief steps you can plunge into shadows as dark and deep as the unknown itself. To that place I've explored in dreams, and have loved since my one and only visit. Berry Pomeroy Castle.'

My silence exasperated him.

'I've precious little time to waste. Guide me. Get me close and I'll do the rest.'

I floundered completely.

'Do this or I'll haunt you, dammit!'

It was a joke of course, but he was serious about his scheme, whatever it was.

'Take me there, and if I die or live, I shall rest content.'

I explained, as gently as possible, that the doctor said he couldn't be moved.

'Ha! I don't need to move. This journey is of the spirit, astral travel, a pilgrimage of the soul. And if it's just imagination, so what? I die happy. But if I can do this, and I actually believe I can – it's amazing – I'll die without dying. Now there's a happy ending worth trying for.'

Now I understood what he wanted. We may be familiar with a Christian priest reading the last rites to a dying parishioner, but in other cultures different words are read. In some, when the ties to life are loosened, and the soul is free to embark on its voyage into the spirit world, the route of the magical journey is described in words of vivid poetry, evoking the natural path of sacred symbolism, leading the purified spirit to dwell with the eternals.

How could I refuse?

'You know the way?' He asked, childlike in sincerity, knowing everything hinged on my answer. 'As if you could drive me there – to the ruined castle?'

Yes, I knew the way.

'Please, be my eyes until we get there. I have the strength to find my way once we arrive, if you can just give me strength to get there first. Guide me, now.'

OK.

He closed his eyes firmly. They would never open again.

'Thank you,' he sighed. 'Leaving this room, do we turn left or right?'

I said it was right, and the simple word filled his little room with affirmation. He smiled.

'How far? Describe everything. In detail.'

I did, and I too closed my eyes to concentrate. There were corridors and stairs, but soon we left the building to stand beneath the orange-tinged underbelly of the night's low cloud (strange how we both agreed it was overcast). As if I were driving out of the town, I narrated the route, and soon we were snaking through the countryside toward the village of Berry Pomeroy.

I'd never been to the castle (I too had always somehow put if off), but I knew the turning from years of driving between Cockington and Totnes. When we arrived at the junction I explained I could lead him no further.

'No need, it's just up here,' he said with the infectious enthusiasm he could always conjure so effortlessly. 'Just along the road... There's the lodge. Now here's the private path leading down through the woods, see how the hill slopes away to the left? I see it like it's daylight – deeply shadowed from the trees, but definitely day. Just like it was.'

Knowing him as well as I did, I could read the tone of his voice and easily imagine the expression on his face.

'We're nearly there.'

I could even tell the way he walked while he spoke, light-footed like a dancer, always ready to pirouette to follow a bird in flight, or to search out the cause of an unexpected sound.

'Thank you, without you I could have got lost, but now I'm sure of the way. Everything shines with a silver light. The castle is just through those trees.'

When we walked into the open ground before the ancient walls, my imagination conjured them from a dozen long-forgotten magazine photos and local TV snippets.

'Last time, at my first sight of the castle, I thrilled with a tingling surge deep in my stomach. That adrenalin release always haunted me because no-one could claim these ruins are majestic or beautiful, but now I see the cause of it. There is an edge here, a perimeter surrounding the whole site. Invisible to mortal eyes, I see it now, a dome like glass, shimmering with pale white fire. Few could walk through it and be unaffected.'

As he spoke I saw it too, glistening like a heat haze, a veil arcing high above the trees and the ruins. Such is the power of suggestion, and on a guided mental journey like this, images can arise as clearly as in a waking dream. But what happened next, although trivial, was like nothing I have experienced before.

'It feels cool,' he continued, 'and calming as I touch it. But this part of the journey is for me alone. Even if it is the hardest thing I've ever asked of you, leave me now. Please, without a word – I couldn't bear it otherwise.'

I opened my mouth to protest.

'No! Don't break the spell! Death awaits me if I return with you. Here I may find my future, my peace, my miracle. Here, I can be free. Retrace your route – it will take but a moment as you travel with the speed of thought. Think yourself back in the room and wriggle your toes. Tell me when you are safely back. Are you there, safely back where we began?'

'Yes.'

It was the first and last lie I ever told him, and I suspected there would be a price to pay, but I simply couldn't leave him. I knew his attention was on entering his dream-come-true. He would never know my deceit.

'The air,' he whispered, 'is thick as scented water. Sounds are crystal clear, sight a thousand times brighter, I move with power and grace. Everything here is alive. The stones of the bare walls are articulated bones, infused with the spirit of the castle that gazes out through windows and doors... This is absolutely holy ground.'

As he described his entry into the energy field I watched and saw his body absorbed. It was as if I had been observing through a magnifying lens, I saw it perfectly and in great detail. But then, as if I gently pulled that magnifying lens away, what I watched grew larger and lost focus. Then, suddenly, his form expanded to fill the entire lens – the entire dome – and was gone in an instant.

My world was turned upside down. Although I still heard his voice as he walked toward the castle, I could no longer see him – he had vanished – become a ghost. I believe it was at that moment that his body died.

I was consumed by an emotion so visceral it wrenched a sob from my body. My eyes opened and I was back at the hospital with my friend's lifeless body lying in the bed. Some equipment started sounding an alarm, and a nurse arrived. Mercifully, she knew of and respected his wish to have no intervention or resuscitation.

I shall always be glad that, whatever actually happened, in his passing he knew no regrets, but was dignified and resolute with the challenge of life triumphantly met.

Nowadays, it is practically a scientific dogma to explain my friend's journey as the unravelling of the mind as it sinks into death – the ultimate triumph of fantasy – entering into a dream-world as prelude to the big sleep. But I sometimes wonder whether that very loosening of the bonds tethering consciousness to the outer world is just the necessary first step in a real and inevitable journey – the final liberation of our spirit from its body?

And, try as I might, I still cannot explain how my imagination could have invented my vision of the way he disappeared into the castle's perimeter forcefield. Sometimes I wonder if what I saw at that moment was actually real – the prize at the end of my journey – a glimpse of a world more strange and wonderful than any I could possibly have imagined.

Now, in the dark watches of the night I wonder if my friend did actually find his way to the one place to which he yearned to return. I find myself hoping he did, and sometimes I even find myself believing.

I am comforted by the knowledge that he would certainly be a powerful protective force for Berry Pomeroy Castle, and his humanity would strive to help anyone who visits the ruin with a weight in their hearts, so they could leave their burden there, and depart released and at peace. And if there was any way to help the spirit of that woman on the stairs, I have no doubt he would use all his considerable strength to release her.

What we believe is, ultimately, a matter of faith, and we are all free to choose; but I have good reason to suppose he may indeed have walked free. Immediately before he led me away on our spirit journey together, something happened to him that many trauma victims report – often saying it was more life-changing than the injuries themselves – he had an out of the body experience. It was, I am sure, the inspiration for that final pilgrimage to Berry Pomeroy Castle.

He had been unconscious for several minutes, but instead of rising to awareness like a sleeper wakening slowly, his eyes flashed open and instantly found mine.

'Wow!' he exclaimed. 'I've been floating by the ceiling, up there.' He gestured to the corner behind me.

'I was looking down on the whole room. My spirit – consciousness, call it what you will – was completely there! I saw everything at once. It was so peaceful.'

Then, chuckling, he told me something shocking but true. I could not deny it even though I had taken pains to conceal it from everybody, absolutely.

'Ha-ha!' He laughed. 'You know you're getting a bald spot – right on top!'

Afterword
Bob Mann

DERYCK SEYMOUR CLAIMED that writing his first book on the castle freed him from its haunting influence, but I can see no such release for me; instead I anticipate years of future work (and I don't mean cynical money-spinning ventures like *The Berry Pomeroy Castle Cook Book* or *Lose Weight with Margaret Pomeroy*).

There are many avenues I'd like to explore further, including the Lovecraft connection mentioned briefly in my story of the 'vision' and 'disappearance.' Everything stated there about the cult American horror and fantasy writer H. P. Lovecraft (1890–1937) is true: on his father's side he was descended from generations of South Devon farm labourers and village craftsmen, living in a wide spread of parishes, but especially in the area between the eastern edge of Dartmoor and the coast, centred on Broadhempston, Woodland, Ipplepen and Torbryan. The spelling 'Lovecraft' is quite late; the name usually appears as 'Lucroft' or 'Lockroft', or some such variant. They were familiar with the streets and pubs of Totnes and Newton Abbot on market days, and may easily have traded, drunk or even mated there with the Manns, Kingwills, Petherbridges, Blights, Widecombes and others of my own ancestry.

On our expedition in May 2010 we found a Lovecraft gravestone at Broadhempston within ten minutes, and celebrated with a pint or two at the Monk's Retreat, which, as the Church House Inn, was once kept by one of Lovecraft's forebears.

Lovecraft, who considered himself very much a gentleman scholar in the 18th century tradition, may not have been too happy if he had realised his family's humble social status; an aunt had told him that he had an ancestral home called Minster Hall (i.e. Church House, get it?), and he appears to have sincerely believed that his background was one of landed gentry. But, as we walked through the lanes from Broadhempston to Woodland, I felt that he would have loved the landscapes they lived and worked in: the deep combes, the rolling hills and fields, and Totnes, with its steep old streets, arrow passages and lazing cats (he was a cat lover, for which I forgive him much). He was deeply attached to his own home city of Providence, Rhode Island, and the old settled countryside of New England, and would have felt at home here (or as at home as a man so highly strung could feel anywhere).

Since that day, I have come to suspect that the strain of insanity running in the family (his father went mad, and the last Devon Lovecraft died in the county lunatic asylum at Exminster in 1911) may have originated with some unspeakable rites performed at the ruins of Berry Pomeroy Castle, probably involving a certain book, the very title of which has the power to unhinge the mind (Lovecraft scholars will know the volume to which I refer; those who are safely ignorant are fortunate in their innocence). A copy of the book could well have been left at the castle in the early 17th century when some North African corsairs, captured whilst ravaging the Devon coast, were briefly held there. If it subsequently came into the hands of semi-literate locals, the consequences could easily have given rise to barely imaginable horrors, and would be more than enough to explain the terrible psychic disturbances experienced at the castle.

The recent discovery of a 'Luckraft' gravestone in Berry Pomeroy churchyard brings my theory a step closer to being provable. There is certainly the germ of a tale here, waiting to be told. But can my own sanity survive the telling?

Maybe, after all, I should leave it to more dedicated Lovecraftians to explore the matter; anyone on that expedition could do it far better than I, and I hesitate to delve too deeply into his world, not least because of what it might do to my prose style.

Whether or not I ever manage to piece that particular story together, I have at least one more that is quietly taking shape in my mind, and, not long ago, I was talking to one of my nieces about the castle (living in Cumbria, she had never heard of it). She asked me to take her to it some time, and I explained how being there with any female loved one always fills me with anxiety for her safety. She immediately responded by suggesting that I take all the women in my life to the castle together, and get it over with all at once. The very thought of doing this in reality fills me with horror, but as an idea for a story it is magnificent.

Then, of course, we have Sue Hinds's novel and the rest of Wendy Ruocco's trilogy to look forward to. I'm also pretty sure that Valerie Belsey has other tales to tell of the castle, and no doubt Laurence Green can find something more to say about its ghostly denizens. And who knows what poetic inspirations it will provide in the future?

So I suspect that a further volume is very much a possibility. If you think you would like to contribute to it, please get in touch. Meanwhile, I've begun to notice, while walking into town from Follaton every day, that an arrangement of trees on one of the hills above me is beginning to look like the two towers of a gatehouse, with a square mansion behind it. And this time it is the right way round. It must be obvious to everyone on the estate but no one else will mention it...

Also available from the Longmarsh Press
Ielfstan's Place

Richard Girling's masterly fictional evocation of life in the Dartmoor parish of Ilsington from the time of the area's earliest human inhabitants to the twentieth century.

First published in 1981, this special thirtieth anniversary edition includes a new introduction by the author.

'I know of no other book about an English village quite like this one... The reader is plunged into a succession of "rural ages," each uniquely strange, haunting and disturbing. It is quite an experience.' **Ronald Blythe**

'Every piece of the mosaic is alive with invention and beautifully visual... like lichen on granite, the character of the hamlet takes hold.' ***The Guardian***

'A haunting fusion of time and locality.' ***Observer***

Ielfstan's Place, **Richard Girling, ISBN 978-0-9561705-1-4, £8.99, pbk, available from bookshops or direct from the Longmarsh Press, 5 Brook View, Follaton, Totnes, Devon TQ9 5FH**